ECDL®

Revision Series

Using Microsoft® Office

Covering:

Word Processing Software

Spreadsheet Software

Database Software

Presentation Software

Release RS17v3

Published by:

CiA Training Ltd
Business & Innovation Centre
Sunderland Enterprise Park
Sunderland SR5 2TA
United Kingdom

Tel: +44 (0) 191 549 5002
Fax: +44 (0) 191 549 9005

E-mail: info@ciatraining.co.uk
Web: www.ciatraining.co.uk

ISBN-13: 978-1-86005-838-7

First published 2010

Copyright © 2010 CiA Training Ltd

All rights reserved. No part of this publication may be reproduced, stored in a retrieval system, or transmitted in any form or by any means (electronic, mechanical, photocopying, recording or otherwise) without the prior written permission of CiA Training Limited.

Microsoft is a registered trademark and Windows is a trademark of the Microsoft Corporation. Screen images and Clip Art reproduced by permission of the Microsoft Corporation. All other trademarks in this book are acknowledged as the property of their respective owners.

European Computer Driving Licence, ECDL, International Computer Driving Licence, ICDL, and related logos are all registered Trade Marks of The European Computer Driving Licence Foundation Limited ("ECDL Foundation").

CiA Training Ltd is an entity independent of The British Computer Society using the name BCS, The Chartered Institute for IT ("BCS") and is not associated with ECDL Foundation or BCS in any manner.

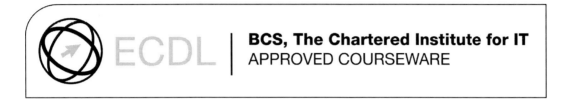

BCS, The Chartered Institute for IT
APPROVED COURSEWARE

This courseware may be used to assist learners to prepare for the ECDL Certification Programme as titled on the courseware. Neither BCS nor **CiA Training Ltd** warrants that the use of this courseware publication will ensure passing of the tests for that ECDL Certification Programme.

This courseware publication has been independently reviewed and approved by BCS as covering the learning objectives for the ECDL Certification Programme.

Confirmation of this approval can be obtained by reviewing www.bcs.org/ecdl.

The material contained in this courseware publication has not been reviewed for technical accuracy and does not guarantee that candidates will pass the test for the ECDL Certification Programme.

Any and all assessment items and/or performance-based exercises contained in this courseware relate solely to this publication and do not constitute or imply certification by BCS or ECDL Foundation in respect of the ECDL Certification Programme or any other ECDL test.

Irrespective of how the material contained in this courseware is deployed, for example in a learning management system (LMS) or a customised interface, nothing should suggest to the candidate that this material constitutes certification or can lead to certification through any other process than official ECDL certification testing.

For details on sitting a test for an ECDL certification programme in the UK, please visit the BCS website at www.bcs.org/ecdl.

Learners using this courseware must be registered with BCS before undertaking a test for ECDL. Without a valid registration, the test(s) cannot be undertaken and no certificate, nor any other form of recognition, can be given to a learner. Registration should be undertaken with BCS at an Approved Centre.

CiA Training's **Revision Exercises** for **ECDL** contain a collection of revision exercises to provide support for students. They are designed to reinforce the understanding of the skills and techniques which have been developed whilst working through CiA Training's corresponding *ECDL* books.

This training, which has been approved by BCS, The Chartered Institute for IT, includes exercise items intended to assist learners in their training for an ECDL Certification Programme. These exercises are not ECDL certification tests. For information about Approved Centres in the UK please visit the BCS website at www.bcs.org/ecdl.

The revision exercises, grouped into sections, cover the following modules:

- Word Processing Software
- Spreadsheet Software
- Database Software
- Presentation Software

A minimum of two revision exercises are included for each section. There are also general exercises which cover techniques from any section within each module. Answers are provided at the end of the guide for all modules.

Aims and Objectives

To provide the knowledge and techniques necessary to be able to successfully utilise the features included within the four modules outlined above. After completing the exercises the user will have experience in the following areas:

- Producing various word processed documents
- Manipulating spreadsheets and charts
- Creating and interrogating databases
- Creating and running presentations

Downloading the Data Files

Data files accompanying this guide allow you to learn and practise new skills without the need for lots of data entry. These files must be downloaded from the Internet. Go to **www.ciatraining.co.uk/data** and follow the simple on-screen instructions.

<u>Your *FastCode* for this guide's data is:</u> **RS17**

By default, the data files will be downloaded to **CIA DATA FILES\Syllabus 5 Revision Series** within the **Documents** library or **My Documents** folder. If you prefer, the data can be supplied on CD at an additional cost. Contact the Sales team at *info@ciatraining.co.uk*.

Office Versions

These revision exercises were written without reference to any specific version of *Microsoft Office*. The data, however, is *Microsoft Office* specific and the correct set of data should be downloaded to match your version of *Office*.

Recommendations

- Read the whole of each exercise before starting to work through it. This ensures understanding of the topic and prevents unnecessary mistakes.

- As screenshots have been captured in the UK, currencies may be shown in £ sterling. In different countries these will be shown in the appropriate currency.

- Some fonts, themes or templates used in this guide may not be available on all computers. If this is the case, select an alternative.

Word Processing Software
Section Exercises

The following revision exercises are divided into sections, each targeted at specific elements of the ECDL module *Word Processing Software*. The individual sections are an exact match for the sections in the ECDL training guides from CiA Training, making the guides an ideal reference source for anyone working through these exercises.

1. Getting Started

These exercises include topics taken from the following list: starting *Word*, recognising the screen layout, using the menus and toolbars or tabs and Quick Access Toolbar, using help features, exiting *Word*.

Exercise 3.1

1. Start *Word*.

2. Depending on the version of *Word*, either hide the **Standard** and **Formatting** toolbars or minimise the **Ribbon**.

3. Redisplay the features hidden in the previous step.

4. Use the help feature to find information about **page orientation**.

5. In the help content, find out which menu or tab would you go to in order to change **page orientation**?

6. Which toolbar or tab would you go to in order to insert **WordArt**?

7. Without using a menu option, what would you need to do to display a toolbar or tab that contains **WordArt** tools?

8. When the mouse pointer is hovering over a button on a toolbar or tab, what is displayed?

9. Exit *Word*.

Exercise 3.2

1. Start *Word*.

2. Use the help feature to find information about **formatting marks**.

3. In the help content, find out which toolbar or tab you would go to in order to show or hide **formatting marks**?

4. Which menu or tab contains the **Hyphenation** feature? Use help if you like.

5. Display the **Paragraph** dialog box. Can this dialog box be resized? Does the dialog box appear on the **Taskbar**?

6. Which of the following can <u>not</u> be set from this dialog box: line spacing, alignment or font colour?

7. Click **Cancel** on the dialog box to remove it.

8. Exit *Word*.

2. Documents

These exercises include topics taken from the following list: entering text, working in different views, opening, saving and closing documents, creating a document from available templates, saving documents in other formats.

Exercise 3.3

1. Start *Word*.

2. Type a few sentences about yourself.

3. Close *Word*. What message is displayed?

4. Click **Cancel** in the message box to cancel the close process.

5. Save the document as **Personal**. What extension is added by default to a saved document in *Word*?

6. Close the document.

7. Open the document **Rich** from the supplied data files. What is the default view for this document.

8. Press <**Enter**> at the end of the text and type an extra line:

   It is therefore a useful format for e-mail messages.

9. Save the document as a **Rich Text Format** file with the same name. What file extension is added?

10. Close the document and reopen **Personal**.

11. Now save the file as a template, named **Personal Info**. What file extension is added?

12. Close the document.

Exercise 3.4

1. Start a new blank document in *Word* and type some text about your hobbies.

2. Switch to **Outline View**.

3. Switch to **Web Layout View**.

4. Return to **Print Layout View** and save in **Works** format (any version), as **Hobbies**. Select **Yes** if prompted about a loss of formatting. What file extension is added by default? Close the document.

5. Close the document and open the document **Plain** from the supplied data files.

6. Press <**Enter**> at the end of the text and type an extra line:

    Plain text files take up the least space of any text file type.

7. Save the document as a **Plain Text** file (or **Text Only** file in *Word 2000*) with a new name, **Very Plain**. What file extension is added?

8. A warning is displayed. Why is this? Click **OK** (or **Yes**) to accept the warning. Close the document.

9. Create a new document based on an available template. Select any **Letter** template and create the document.

10. Make a few changes and then save it as **My Letter**.

11. Close *Word*.

3. Editing Text

These exercises include topics taken from the following list: inserting and deleting text, selecting words and sentences, selecting lines and paragraphs, inserting special characters and symbols, using undo and redo, showing and hiding non printing characters, inserting and deleting soft carriage returns.

Exercise 3.5

1. Open the document **Gardens**.

2. Insert the registered symbol, ®, after **Gardens** in the title.

3. Insert a formatting control (manual line break) in the heading, between **Toffington Gardens** and **Grand Opening** so that each part appears on a separate line but the whole title will still be considered as a single paragraph.

4. Use a button to display non printing characters. What is the symbol for the control added in the last step?

   a) ¶   b) ↵   c) ✳

5. Insert a paragraph break at the end of the first sentence.

6. Insert a blank line after this to separate it from the next paragraph.

7. Place the cursor in the last sentence of the third paragraph. What key combination will select the whole sentence?

8. Select the whole sentence and delete it.

9. Click the **Undo** button. What happens?

10. In the second paragraph, select the word **estate** and replace it with **grounds**.

11. In the fifth paragraph, insert the word **relaxing** before the word **picnic**.

12. Start a new paragraph at the end of the document and enter the copyright symbol (©), then type **Toffington Publications 2009**.

13. Remove the soft carriage return in the heading.

14. Save the document as **Gardens2** and close it.

Exercise 3.6

1. Open the document **Ballet**.

2. Replace the word **veteran** with **experienced** and the word **troupe** with **company** by overtyping.

3. Insert a soft carriage return between the two sentences of the first paragraph.

4. Insert the registered symbol after **Barnacle Ballet Company**.

5. Insert the trademark symbol after **Duck Pond** in the title.

6. Select the whole paragraph starting **All proceeds** and delete it.

7. Insert the following three paragraphs of text at the end of the document:

> Not advisable for those of a nervous disposition
>
> ♫ Music by the accomplished composer Ivor Stringvesto
>
> ⓘ For more information visit our web site

Note: *The symbols used can be found in the Webdings font.*

8. Merge the first 2 of these new paragraphs.

9. Use a key press to select the entire document. What is it?

10. Press the **q** key. What happens?

11. Click **Undo** to retrieve the document content. Redo the deletion.

12. Finally, undo the deletion.

13. Display the formatting marks. What does the mark · indicate?

14. Insert a tab at the front of each paragraph.

15. Save the document as **Ballet2** and close it.

4. Printing

These exercises include topics taken from the following list: previewing a document, printing a document, printing parts of a document, and printing specific pages.

Exercise 3.7

1. Open the document **Hall**.

2. Select **Print Preview** (or **Print** in *Office 2010/2013*), and make sure the display shows one full page only.

3. Zoom into the page to enlarge it.

4. Zoom back out again to the previous magnification and show one full page only.

5. Close **Print Preview** (or **Print** in *Office 2010/2013*).

6. Select the section of the document describing the house (with the sub-heading) and print a copy of this section only.

7. Close the document <u>without</u> saving.

Exercise 3.8

1. Open the document **Viruses**.

2. Select **Print Preview** (or **Print** in *Office 2010/2013*).

3. Show a multiple page view showing two pages side by side (zoom out in *Office 2010/2013* until two pages appear).

4. Change the **Zoom** value to **50**%.

5. Close **Print Preview** and print a copy of page **2** of the document only.

6. Print two copies of the first paragraph of the document, including the item title.

7. Close the document <u>without</u> saving.

5.   Formatting Text

These exercises include topics taken from the following list: underlining, emboldening and italicising text, changing fonts and text size, applying text effects, subscript and superscript, using the format painter, cutting, copying and pasting.

Exercise 3.9

1. Open the **LakeDistrict** document.

2. Change the font of the entire document to **Tahoma**.

3. Change the size of the title, **The English Lake District**, to **14pt**, **upper case** and **Bold**.

4. Select the first subheading, **Rocks**, and format it as **Bold** and **Underlined**.

5. Change the colour of this subheading to **dark green**.

6. Use a button to apply all this formatting to the other subheadings, **Glaciation** and **Civilisation**.

7. In the last section, italicise the first word in each of the last four paragraphs (**Agriculture**, **Forestry**, **Mining**, **Tourism**).

8. Change the font of the first paragraph of text to **Verdana** and apply formatting of **Italic** and a colour of **dark green**.

9. Use editing commands to move the entire first paragraph to the end of the document so that it becomes the last paragraph.

10. Save the document as **Lakes2** and close it.

Exercise 3.10

1. Start a blank *Word* document and type the following text:

    The British Banking System is now heavily committed to the use of computers in order to give a much faster and more effective service to the increasing number of people who now have bank accounts.

    The banks are making increasing use of cashpoint machines. These are special computer terminals, connected to the bank's computer, which allow customers to withdraw money and make use of other banking services outside of normal banking hours.

2. Format the entire document as **Century Gothic, 12pt**.

3. Copy the text **British Banking System** and paste it as a title to the text.

4. **Underline** the title and change it to upper case.

5. Make the text **British Banking System** in the first sentence **italic** and **red**.

6. Use the format painter to copy this formatting to the word **cashpoint**.

7. On a new line at the end of the document type the text **A ceiling**. Press the **<Tab>** key twice and type **B floor**.

8. Change the font size of the new line to **18pt**.

9. Format the words **ceiling** and **floor** as **Superscript** and **Subscript** respectively.

10. Change the colour of the whole line to **dark blue**.

11. Save the document as **Banks2** and close it.

6.   Tools

These exercises include topics taken from the following list: checking spelling, hyphenating text, searching for text, replacing text, using the zoom control, and changing preferences.

Exercise 3.11

1. Open the document **Tours**.

2. Check the item for spelling mistakes and repeated words.

3. Replace mistakes by making a choice from the suggestions.

4. **LearnersVille** is a name, not a spelling mistake. Ignore this.

5. Hyphenate the document automatically.

6. Add your name as the **Author** for the document.

7. Replace all occurrences of the name **LearnersVille** with the name of the town/city where you live.

8. Replace the phrase **day and night** with **24/7**.

9. Save the document as **Tours2** and close it.

Exercise 3.12

1. Open the document **Hall**.

2. Change the **Zoom** setting to **Whole Page** (**One Page** in *2007/2010/2013*). What is a disadvantage of this view?

3. Change the **Zoom** setting to **Page Width**. What is a disadvantage of this view?

4. Change the **Zoom** setting to **100%**.

5. Check the document for spelling mistakes. Although there should be no actual mistakes, several names will be highlighted as unrecognised words. Which different names are highlighted? Add each one to the dictionary as it appears.

6. Search for the phrase **a treat from the tea room**. Which page is it found on?

7. Search for the first occurrence of the word **folly**. Which section is it in?

8. Replace every occurrence of the word **house** in the document with the word **hall**. How many replacements are made?

9. Check the preferences (options) for the document and note down the default location for the saving and retrieval of normal documents.

10. Change the default location to the **CIA DATA FILES** folder.

11. Return the opening and saving preferences to the default location.

12. Close the document <u>without</u> saving.

7. Formatting Paragraphs

These exercises include topics taken from the following list: aligning text, indenting paragraphs, applying advanced indentation, applying bullets and numbers, changing line and paragraph spacing, applying and changing tab settings, changing tab alignment, and applying borders.

Exercise 3.13

1. Open the document **LakeDistrict** and zoom to **100%**.

2. What is the best way to align text:

    a) use the indent and align tools, or the <**Tab**> key?

    b) use spaces?

3. **Centre** align the title and make it **Bold**.

4. Apply a left indentation of **1cm** to the whole of the first paragraph.

5. Apply a left indentation of **1cm** to the first line <u>only</u> in each of the next 4 paragraphs.

6. Select the whole document and apply a spacing of **6pt** to appear after every paragraph.

7. In the **Glaciation** section is a list of seven examples, starting with **Hanging Valleys**. Make this a bulleted list using any bullet character.

8. Apply an alignment of **Justified** to the bulleted list.

9. In the **Civilisation** section, make the last four paragraphs into a list numbered **1. 2. 3.** and **4**.

10. Increase the line spacing for the first paragraph of the document to **1.5** lines.

11. Add a **1pt box** border to the same paragraph.

12. Save the document as **Lakes3**.

13. Remove the bullets and numbering from the document.

14. Undo the deletion of the bullets and numbers.

15. Save and close the document with the same name.

Exercise 3.14

1. Spacing between paragraphs can be created using the <**Return**> key. However, this is not good practice - what is a better way?

2. Create a blank document in *Word*.

3. Set left aligned tab stops at positions **4cm** and **8cm**.

4. Enter the text **Name Department Telephone** using the **Tab** key so that the word **Department** lines up with the first tab stop and **Telephone** lines up with the second. Press <**Enter**> to end the line.

5. On the next line enter the text **John Smith Admin 432** using the **Tab** key so that **Admin** lines up under **Department** and **432** lines up under **Telephone**.

6. Enter the following lines in the same manner:

   Tracy Jones   Sales   135
   Tariq Hussan   Admin   446
   Nina Kurpova   Sales   158

7. Change the line spacing to **Double** for the whole document.

8. Move the tab stop positions for the whole list to **6cm** and **13cm**.

9. Change the **13cm** tab to be **Right** aligned.

10. Change the **Right Indent** for the whole list to **1.24cm** (or set it to **14cm** on the ruler).

11. Apply a **1pt Box** border to the whole list.

12. Apply a shading of **Gray 10%** to the list.

13. Make the first line of the list **Bold**.

14. Save the document as **List2** and close it.

15. Open the document **Overtime List** and change the tabs as indicated on the top line.

16. Adjust the spacing of the tabs if necessary to improve the layout.

17. Increase the spacing above each line to **6pt**.

18. Save the document as **Overtime List2** and close it.

8. Multiple Documents

These exercises include topics taken from the following list: switching between open documents, cutting, copying and pasting between documents, applying headers and footers, and applying page numbering.

Exercise 3.15

1. Open the document **Gardens**, then open the document **Hall**.

2. Use a menu option or tab to switch to the **Gardens** document again. Which menu or tab button is required?

3. Format the whole **Gardens** document as **Arial** font with **Double** line spacing.

4. At the end of the document leave a blank line then add the sentence:
   Visitors can also take a tour of the main Toffington Hall buildings.

5. Switch to the **Hall** document and copy the three paragraphs of text under the **House** subheading.

6. Switch back to the **Gardens** document and paste the text starting on a new line after the newly added sentence.

7. Make sure the newly added text has the same formatting as the previous paragraphs.

8. Enter your name as a text entry in the centre of the document **Header**.

9. Enter an automatic page number field in the centre of the document **Footer** and a date field at the right.

10. In the **Header**, edit your name to your first initial and surname only.

11. Print a copy of the complete document.

12. Save the **Gardens** document as **Gardens3**, then close it.

13. Close the **Hall** document <u>without</u> saving.

Exercise 3.16

1. Create a new blank document.

2. Open the **LakeDistrict** document.

3. Cut the section on **Rocks** from the **LakeDistrict** document.

4. Switch to the blank document and paste the cut text.

5. Save the new document as **Rocks2**.

6. View the **Header** and insert the **Filename** of the document as an **Autotext** field on the left of the area.

7. View the **Footer**. Insert the **Author**, **Page Number** and **Date** as fields at the left, centre and right of the footer line.

8. In which of the four main views, **Normal (Draft)**, **Web Layout**, **Print Layout** and **Outline**, will the headers and footers be visible?

9. Print a copy of the **Rocks2** document.

10. Save the **Rocks2** document then close it.

11. Close the **LakeDistrict** document <u>without</u> saving.

9.   Tables

These exercises include topics taken from the following list: inserting tables, entering text into tables, selecting cells, changing column width, inserting and deleting cells, inserting and deleting rows and columns, and applying borders.

Exercise 3.17

1. Open a new blank document and insert a table of 4 columns and 7 rows.

2. Enter the following data into the table (as shown overleaf).

Name	Continent	Range	Height(m)
Everest	Asia	Himalayas	8850
Annapurna	Asia	Himalayas	8091
Aconcagua	South America	Andes	6962
Mount McKinley	North America	Alaskan	6194
Kilimanjaro	Africa	Volcano	5895
Mont Blanc	Europe	Alps	4807

3. Format all the table content as **Arial 12pt** and make sure all borders are displayed.

4. Insert a new column on the right of the table with a heading of **First Ascent**.

5. Add data **1953**, **1950**, **1897**, **1913**, **1889**, **1786** down the column.

6. Format the first row content as **Bold** and **Centred**.

7. Adjust the width of the columns if necessary so that all data is displayed and each cell only requires a single line.

8. Apply a **1½ pt** box border to the first row.

9. Apply a **Gray-15%** shading to the first row.

10. Apply a shading of **palest green** to the remaining cells of the table.

11. Save the document as **Mountains**.

12. Delete the final column, **First Ascent** then save and close the document. You may have to reapply the border.

Exercise 3.18

1. Start a new blank document in *Word* and enter a centred title of **Maintenance Log**.

2. Insert a table of 2 columns and 4 rows.

3. Type the column headers **Date** and **Name**.

4. Insert a new column after **Name** and add the header **Action Taken**.

5. Specify the three column widths as **3cm**, **4cm** and **7cm** respectively. Ensure the table is centred on the page.

6.   Enter the following information :

12/04/09   Jim Dawson   Door handle repaired in office 10a

16/08/09   Jim Dawson   Broken window in 1st floor break room replaced

23/08/09   Amy Madson   Broken chair in conference room 2 replaced

7.   Edit the data for 16/08/09 to **2nd floor break room**.

8.   Widen the **Action Taken** column as required so that all the data in each row is displayed and shown on a single line.

9.   Insert a new row at the bottom of the table and enter the following information: **27/08/09 Frank Carter Broken light switch fixed in corridor**.

10.   Set the height of all rows to be **0.7**.

11.   Remove all borders and add a **1½pt** box border around the whole table.

12.   Delete the bottom row of the table.

13.   Insert a few blank lines after the table.

14.   Create the following table (as shown overleaf). The text is all **Arial 12pt bold** except **Total** which is **Arial 14pt bold**. The shading is all **Gray - 20%** except **Total** which is **Gray - 35%**. The cell to the right of **Total** has a **1½pt** border.

	• **Weekly Time Sheet**		
• **Employee**			
•	• **Hours Worked**	• **Signature**	
• **Mon**	•	•	
• **Tues**	•	•	
• **Wed**	•	•	
• **Thur**	•	•	
• **Fri**	•	•	
• **Total**	•	•	

15.   Save the document as **Log** and close it.

10. Document Manipulation

These exercises include topics taken from the following list: selecting paper size, changing page orientation, changing margins, inserting page breaks, and applying styles.

Exercise 3.19

1. Open the document **LakeDistrict**.

2. Change the **Left** and **Right** page margins to **4cm**.

3. Change the **Top** and **Bottom** page margins to **3cm**.

4. Set the orientation to **Landscape**.

5. Insert page breaks before the **Glaciation** and **Civilisation** subheadings.

6. Apply the style **Heading1** to the main title of the document.

7. Apply the style **Heading2** to the subheadings, **Rocks**, **Glaciation** and **Civilisation**.

8. Apply the style **Green** to the first letter of each word in the title.

9. Print a copy of the document.

10. Change the orientation to **Portrait**.

11. Delete the page break before **Glaciation**.

12. Save the document as **Lakes4** and close it.

Exercise 3.20

1. When you want to create a new page in a document is it better to use returns, or to insert a page break?

2. Open the document **Hall**.

3. Change the paper size to **Letter**.

4. Select the whole document and apply the style **Halltext**.

5. Apply the style **Hallhead** to the main title for the document.

6. Apply the style **Hallsub** to the first subtitle in the document (**The House**).

7. Use format painter to apply the **Hallsub** style to all other subtitles in the document.

8. Set the top page margin only to **5cm**.

9. Insert **Page Breaks** before the subheadings **The Gardens** and **Pets' Corner**.

10. Save the document as **Hall2** and close it.

11. Is there any limit to the number of page breaks that can be inserted on a single page?

12. What are the two types of page orientation called?

11. Mail Merge

These exercises include topics taken from the following list: creating a main document, creating a data source, editing the main document, and performing mail merge.

Exercise 3.21

1. In a new blank document, type the following letter which is to be the main document of a mail merge. Leave spaces in place of each item of bracketed text.

> **(Title) (First Name) (Last Name)**
> **(Address Line 1)**
>
> **Dear (First Name)**
>
> **Congratulations (First Name). You have been uniquely selected to receive one of our completely free holidays. Contact us on the number below and wait for your tickets.**
>
> **Yours sincerely**
>
> **Dawn Waldram**
>
> **791 512116673**

2. Save the document as **Offer**.

3. Create a data source file (recipients list) containing the field names **Title**, **First Name**, **Surname** (or **Last Name**) and **Address Line 1**.

4. Add three fictitious names and addresses to the file. Save this data source (recipient list) as **Test** in the supplied data folder.

5. Insert the data source field names in the appropriate positions in the **Offer** document and save the document again.

6. Merge the **Offer** document and the **Test** data source to produce three letters.

7. Print a copy of the three letters.

8. Save the resulting merged file as **Letters3**.

9. Close all files, saving if prompted.

Exercise 3.22

1. Open the document **Interview**. Instead of sending this letter to one person it is to be used in a mail merge operation.

2. Assign the **Interview** document as the main document in a mail merge process.

3. Open the file **Applicants** as the data source (recipients list).

4. Edit the data and delete the record for **Rula Petrovka**.

5. Change the interview time for Tom Clinkard to **11:00**.

6. Add your own details to the list. Your interview is for the position of **Operator** at **10:00** on **Wednesday 7th September**.

7. Delete all the data from the **Interview** document which is specific to **Ron Springs**, and replace it with the relevant merge fields from the data source.

8. Merge the **Interview** document and the **Applicants** data source to produce four letters.

9. Print a copy of the four letters.

10. Save the resulting merged file as **Letters4**.

11. Close all files <u>without</u> saving.

12. Start a new document and perform a merge operation to create mailing labels, using the **Applicants** data source.

13. Insert all fields on to the first label and copy this to all the other labels.

14. Print one page of address labels.

15. Close all documents <u>without</u> saving.

12. Objects

These exercises include topics taken from the following list: inserting a picture, inserting an image from file, inserting charts, moving and resizing a picture, image or chart.

Exercise 3.23

1. Open the document **Ballet**.

2. Position the cursor on the blank line underneath the title.

3. Locate and insert the clip art image of a duck as shown here.

4. If this clip art cannot be located there is a copy in the supplied data files named **duck.gif**. This can be inserted from file instead.

5. Select the image and resize it to approximately **8cm** by **4cm**.

6. Cut the picture from its current location and paste it on a new line at the end of the document.

7. Copy the image and paste the copy alongside the original.

8. Resize the first image using the handle in the centre of the top edge until it is half the height but the same width.

9. Resize the copied image using the handle in the centre of the right edge until it is half the width but the same height.

10. Which handle would be used to resize the image and maintain its proportions?

11. Copy the second image and paste it into a new document.

12. Save the original document as **Ballet3** and close it.

13. Close the second document <u>without</u> saving.

Exercise 3.24

1. Start a new *Word* document.

2. Type the following heading (centred and bold):

Outdoor Supplies Company

Sales Performance (thousands)

3. Insert a chart under this heading using the following datasheet.

	Qtr 1	Qtr 2	Qtr 3	Qtr 4
Clothing	25	32	39	44
Equipment	16	26	33	30

4. Change the size of the chart, maintaining the aspect ratio, until it is approximately **7cm** high.

5. Centre the chart on the page.

6. Insert 3 blank lines after the chart and then insert the image **Outdoor.gif** from the supplied data.

7. Resize the **Outdoor** image to be **4cm** high.

8. Format the **Outdoor** image to have a **Layout** of **Square**.

9. Move the **Outdoor** image into the top right corner of the page.

10. Save the document as **Outdoor**.

11. Cut the **Outdoor** image and paste it into a new document.

12. From the new document, copy the image and paste it into the top right corner of the **Outdoor** document.

13. Save **Outdoor** and close it.

14. Delete the image and close the remaining document <u>without</u> saving.

Word Processing Software
General Exercises

The following revision exercises can involve processes from any part of the ECDL module *Word Processing Software*.

Exercise 3.25

1. The bar that contains information such as the page and section number of the current page is called what?

    a) Menu Bar

    b) Toolbar

    c) Scroll Bar

    d) Status Bar

    Ensure this bar is displayed.

2. Start a new *Word* document based on the default template and change the paper size to **Letter**.

3. Type the following verses. Make the title and each verse a separate paragraph with soft returns at the end of the first three lines of each verse.

    Jack and Jill

    Jack and Jill went up the hill
    To fetch a pail of water;
    Jack fell down and broke his crown,
    And Jill came tumbling after.

    Up Jack got and home did trot,
    As fast as he could caper;
    Went to bed and bound his head,
    With vinegar and brown paper.

4. Make the title **bold**, **centred** and **underlined**. *Undo* the underline formatting and then *redo* it.

5. View non printing characters and remove any blank lines from the text, then apply formatting so that there is a **12pt** space after each paragraph.

6. Change the font of the whole document to **Comic Sans MS**.

7. Use the **Help** function to find out how to insert clipart. Insert a relevant clipart picture below the text and resize to a suitable size.

8. **Centre** the text of the verses and the picture and save the document as **Rhyme** in rich text format.

9. Open the document **Apply**. This is a general job application letter that is going to be sent out to several companies who have been advertising vacancies. The letters are to be produced using a mail merge process.

10. Add your address and the date as **right justified** lines of text above the first line of the document.

11. Change the font of the whole document to **Arial 12pt** and **justify** the main text of the letter.

12. Replace the name **Emma Jones** with your own. Spell check the document and correct any misspellings. Any real names can be added to the dictionary.

13. Create the following data source:

Contact	Company	Vacancy
Ms Chapman	Metal Products	Shift Manager
Mr Ridley	Ridley Engineering	Team Leader
Mr Rigg	Consolidated Chickens	Supervisor

14. Save the data source as **Vacancies**.

15. Add the fields to the **Apply** document so that the contact, company and vacancy appear in the appropriate places in the letter. Save the letter as **Apply2**.

16. Mail merge the **Apply2** document and the **Vacancies** data source.

17. Preview the resultant letters and then print the document. Save the merged document as **Applications**.

18. Create mailing labels using the same data source and print a single page of labels.

19. Close any open documents <u>without</u> saving.

Exercise 3.26

1. Start *Word* and a new document based on a memo template. Zoom to **100%** and add the details shown below. Save as **My Memo** and close the document. If there is no memo template available in *Word 2007/2010/2013* (you will need to be online), use a fax template.

Memorandum

To: Bob

CC: Brian

From: Dawn

Date: 28/07/2009

Re: Lunch arrangements

Office Cover

Could you please confirm with me each morning, before 10am, which lunch hour you will be taking, so I can ensure adequate cover for answering phones, etc.

Thanks

---

2. Open the document **Holiday Plan** and apply automatic hyphenation.

3. Replace all occurrences of **AnyTown** with **Learnersville**

4. **Underline** and **centre** align the title.

5. Change the font of the whole document to **Arial, 12pt**.

6. Divide the text into paragraphs after the word **visit** (second sentence) and after the word **beach** (in the list of places).

7. Press <**Enter**> before each of the items in the list of places to visit so that the places become a vertical list.

8. Format the list as a bulleted list and change the case of the items in the list so that every word is capitalised. Ensure it is formatted as **Arial 12pt**.

9. Add a **6pt** space after all paragraphs in the document.

---

10. Insert the image file **Beach** underneath the text. **Centre** the image and enlarge it so that is **5cm** high.

11. Underneath the image, add a centred underlined title of **Timetable**. Use a key press to make sure this title always appears at the top of a new page.

12. Add the following data into a table underneath the title. Make sure it is **Arial 12pt**. Shade the top row and the left column **Pale Blue**.

Day	AM	PM
Mon	Beach	Harbour
Tue	Beach	Shopping
Wed	Art Gallery	Museum
Thurs	County Fair	County Fair
Fri	Harbour	Park
Sat	Beach	Shopping

13. Underneath the table, add a centred underlined title of **Weather Forecast** in **Arial 12pt**. Make sure this title always appears at the top of a new page. Add a chart after the title using the following data:

	Mon	Tue	Wed	Thu	Fri	Sat
% chance Sun	70	50	20	50	70	90
% chance Rain	30	50	80	50	30	10

14. Increase the chart width so that all data and labels are fully displayed.

15. Set the page margins to **2.5cm**.

16. Change preferences to set your name as the document author.

17. In the document footer, add the date to the left and page numbers on the right. In the centre of the header, type © **Learnersville Council 2009**.

18. Preview the document and then print one copy of the document.

19. Save the document with a new name, as **Holiday Plan2** and close it.

Exercise 3.27

1. Open the document **Report**. This the draft for a report created by Learnersville council concerning the popularity of existing facilities and suggestions for new ones. It requires some work before it can be submitted.

2. Apply the style **Reporthead** to the title and then apply the character style **Bright** to the first letter of each word in the title.

3. Apply the style **Reporttext** to the remaining text.

4. Insert a table of 4 columns and 5 rows between the first and second paragraphs of text.

5. Enter the following text into the table (you will need to add an extra column).

Facility	Visitors	Enjoyed	Disliked	Neutral
Harbour	560	70%	10%	20%
Beach	850	80%	5%	15%
Art Gallery	436	72%	20%	8%
Park	320	40%	55%	5%

6. Add the following extra row to the table and amend column widths as necessary.

County Fair	510	65%	15%	20%

7. Embolden the top row and increase the height of this row only to twice it's original height.

8. Shade the top row **dark blue** and change the text colour of the top row to **white**.

9. Insert a chart after the second paragraph of text, based on the following datasheet:

	Aquarium	Pier	Zoo	Other
Votes	214	552	130	94

10. If necessary, by dragging only the side edge of the final chart, resize it to be almost the full width of the text (about **15cm** wide).

11. Make sure the third paragraph, starting **Also included**, always starts on a new page.

12. Locate the image **Beach** from the supplied data and insert it after the end of this paragraph. Centre the image on the page and resize the picture, making it **8cm** wide.

13. Cut the text for the complete letter at the end of the **Report** document and paste it into a new blank document.

14. Change the font of the new document to **Arial 12pt black**.

15. Save this document as **Thanks**.

16. The letter is to be merged with the names and addresses in the file **Names**. Include the merge fields **Name**, **Address**, **Town** above the text **Dear Visitor**.

17. Amend the data source to add your own name and address. Merge the document and data source and print the first two merged letters.

18. Save the merged document as **Thanksmerge**, then close it. Don't save the other merge documents.

19. Print one copy of the **Report** document, save it as **Report2** and close it.

Exercise 3.28

1. Open the document **Science** and switch to **Outline View**. This is the first part of a school science project.

2. Add a new first line, **Biology Project - Bill Barnacle** as the title for the project.

3. Switch back to **Print Layout** view and centre the title text. Underline the title and change the font size to **14**. Apply a black box border to this title paragraph and shade it with pale green.

4. Indent the first line of the first paragraph by **1.5 cm**.

5. Search for the word **Biology**. How many occurrences are there? Replace the word **Biology** with **Science** throughout.

6. Use the data in the composition table to create a chart directly underneath it. Increase the width of the chart only, until all the labels on the axes can be seen. Centre the chart on the page.

7. Insert a page break before the last line of text on the page.

8. Insert a new line after the last line of text and create left tabs at **4** cm and **10** cm.

9. Using those tabs, create a tabbed list from the following:

Oxygen	**O2**
Nitrogen	**N2**
Argon	**Ar**
Carbon Dioxide	**CO2**
Neon	**Ne**
Helium	**He**
Methane	**CH4**
Krypton	**Kr**
Hydrogen	**H2**

10. Make the list into a bulleted list using any symbol as the bullets. Apply a **3pt box** border around the list.

11. Format the list to have a right indent of **3cm** and a **6pt** after paragraph spacing.

12. For every symbol in the list where a number occurs, e.g. **O2**, format the number as a subscript, e.g. **O_2**.

13. Locate the entries for carbon dioxide and methane and format them as **italic**. The list should now look something like this:

• Oxygen	O_2
• Nitrogen	N_2
• Argon	Ar
• *Carbon Dioxide*	*CO_2*
• Neon	Ne
• Helium	He
• *Methane*	*CH_4*
• Krypton	Kr
• Hydrogen	H_2

14. Select the whole document and change the font to **Arial** and the line spacing to **1.5** lines.

15. Select the first two paragraphs and justify the text. Add page numbers to the right of the document footer and print a copy of the document.

16. Change the page orientation to **Landscape** and print another copy.

17. Change back to **Portrait** orientation and save the document as a template named **Science2**.

18. Save the document again with a new name, **Science Text** in text format (***.txt** extension). What is the problem with saving in this format? Close and reopen the document to see.

19. Close the document.

Exercise 3.29

1. Start a new *Word* document and display non printing characters. This is to be a mail merged letter sent out to patients of a health centre, informing them of their appointments and requesting the completion of a questionnaire.

2. Type the following text:

LearnersVille Health Centre

LearnersVille

LV4 53F

Date

Dear

You have successfully reserved the following appointment time   on   . You will be seeing   . Please let us know   hours before the appointment if you are unable to attend.

Please find enclosed a short questionnaire to help us improve facilities for visitors to the health centre. If you could bring the completed form with you we would be most grateful.

Yours sincerely

LearnersVille Health Centre.

3. Format the letter as **Arial 10pt** and justify the main body of text and save the document as **Appointment**.

4. Create the following data source as a sample for the merge process and save it as **Patients**:

Title	Initial	Last name	Time	Date	Staff	Hours
Mr	F	Bathurst	11:00am	11/09/09	Dr Chapman	48
Miss	J	Lilly	09:00am	16/10/09	Nurse Rigg	24
Ms	L	Grant	03:00pm	24/10/09	Dr Waldram	48

5. Insert the field headers at the relevant sections and mail merge the two documents together. Save the merged documents as **Appointment Letters**.

6. Switch to the document **Appointment** and then close all open documents <u>without</u> saving.

7. Open the document **Questionnaire**. Underline, embolden and centre the first line. Change the font for the whole document to **Verdana**.

8. Format the first two questions only to have a right indentation of **4cm**. This will leave space for answers to be entered.

9. In the table make the top row bold and the give the left hand column a **pale green** background. Add a **1.5pt** border around all the remaining cells, i.e. the cells where input is possible.

10. On the line with the **Age range** question, add left tab marks at **5cm**, **7.5cm**, **10cm** and **12.5cm** then insert tabs so that the four ranges line up with them.

11. Add a new line under this with the same tab marks, and insert four ⬜ symbols so that they line up under the four ranges. The symbol can be found in the **Wingdings** font. Change the font size for this line to **20pt**.

12. Open the **News** document. Copy all the text and paste it at the end of the **Questionnaire** document.

13. Copy the existing formatting of the **Questionnaire** document to the new text using the format painter.

14. Copy the Health Centre logo from the **News** document and place it after the end of the text in the **Questionnaire** document.

15. Close the **News** document <u>without</u> saving.

16. In the **Questionnaire** document, delete the **News Flash** title.

17. Make the list of alternative locations into a numbered list and right align the image.

18. View the document header. Insert the word **Questionnaire** at the left of the header and insert the current date as a field at the right.

19. Print one copy of the document, then save the document as **Questionnaire2** and close it.

Spreadsheet Software
Section Exercises

The following revision exercises are divided into sections, each targeted at specific elements of the ECDL module *Spreadsheet Software*. The individual sections are an exact match for the sections in the ECDL training guides from CiA Training, making the guides an ideal reference source for anyone working through these exercises.

13. Getting Started

These exercises include topics taken from the following list: starting and closing *Excel*, using menus, toolbars, tabs and help, the worksheet window, moving around a worksheet and setting preferences. There may be optional questions to cope with the differences between *Excel XP/2003* and *Excel 2007/2010/2013*.

Exercise 4.1

1. Start *Excel* using the **Start** button.

2. Use the mouse pointer to find **ToolTips** for the following buttons which can be found on the **Standard** toolbar (*XP/2003*) or the **Home** tab (*2007/2010/2013*).

   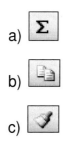

   a) Σ

   b)

   c)

3. On which toolbar or tab is the **Insert Hyperlink** button, ?

4. Use the **Help** function to display the help window and find information about the **Print Preview** process.

5. Display the **Options** for the current session and enter your own name as the **User name**.

6. Display the **Properties** for the current file (document) and enter **William Shakespeare** as the **Author**.

7. Close *Excel*.

Exercise 4.2

1. Start *Excel*. Make sure a blank workbook is displayed.

2. How many worksheets are present in the workbook?

3. Select cell **A1** and press the **Enter** key. Which cell is highlighted now?

4. Use the mouse pointer to find **ToolTips** for the following buttons which can be found on the **Formatting** toolbar (*XP/2003*) or the **Home** tab (*2007/2010/2013*).

a)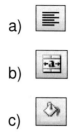

b)

c)

5. With a key press move to the last column of a blank worksheet. What did you press?

6. Move down to the last row, what is the row number?

7. What key press combination always returns to a cell **A1**?

8. What key press combination is used to move one screen to the right?

9. Use **Help** to find out the maximum number of columns in a worksheet (**worksheet size**).

10. In **Options**, note down the default folder for saving and opening workbooks. Change the default folder to **CIA DATA FILES**.

11. Change the default folder location back to its original setting.

12. Close down *Excel*.

14. Open and Close Workbooks

These exercises include topics taken from the following list: opening and closing workbooks, using scroll bars and opening multiple workbooks.

Exercise 4.3

1. Start *Excel* and open the workbook **Grand Hotel**. Maximise the window if necessary.

2. Use the scroll bars to navigate to the edges of the main block of occupied cells. What is the last cell reference (bottom right corner) in the main block?

3. Navigate to the **Bookings** block to the right. What range of cells does it occupy (excluding the **Bookings** label in cell **Q2**)?

4. What is the current rate of **Tax** for **Jan to Mar**, located in cell **R17**, as a percentage?

5. Make **A1** the active cell in the **Grand Hotel** workbook.

6. Scroll down with the scroll button to display **Row 15** as the first row on the screen. What cell contents are displayed at the top left of the screen?

7. Leave the **Grand Hotel** workbook open and open the workbook **Budget**.

8. What is the total **Net Profit** for the year?

9. Make **Grand Hotel** the active workbook.

10. Close the workbook **Grand Hotel** <u>without</u> saving.

11. Close the workbook **Budget** <u>without</u> saving.

Exercise 4.4

1. Open the workbook **Hydrogen**.

2. Open the workbook **Market Stall**.

3. Both the workbooks are now open. The **Taskbar** along the bottom of the screen shows each open workbook as a button.

4. Which of the workbooks is active?

5. Click on the **Hydrogen** button to view that workbook. This workbook is now active.

6. Open the workbook **Temperatures**. The **Taskbar** now shows three open workbooks.

7. Which workbook on the **Taskbar** is active?

8. Display **Market Stall**.

9. Use the scroll bars to navigate to the edges of the block of occupied cells. Which is the last occupied cell?

10. Use a key press to return to cell **A1**. What did you press?

11. Close all the open workbooks <u>without</u> saving.

15. Creating and Saving Workbooks

These exercises include topics taken from the following list: starting a new workbook, entering numbers and labels, saving a new workbook, saving a named workbook and saving as a web page.

Exercise 4.5

1. A spreadsheet containing international customer details has the whole address for each record in one cell. Why is this not good practice?

2. Start a new workbook.

3. Create the following worksheet in the columns and rows indicated.

	A	B	C	D	E
1	Breakdown of TV Viewing Figures				
2					
3		Channel	Percentage		
4		Channel1	28		
5		Channel2	17		
6		Channel3	45		
7		Channel4	6		
8		Channel5	4		
9					

4. Save the workbook as **Viewing**.

5. Resave the workbook as **Viewing.csv** and close it.

6. Open the generic file **snackdata.csv**.

7. Save the file as a workbook **snackdata**.

8. Close the workbook.

Exercise 4.6

1. A list of data should contain blank rows and columns. True or false?

2. Start a new workbook.

3. Create the following worksheet in the columns and rows indicated.

	A	B	C	D
1	CLIMATE	Adelaide, Australia		
2		RAINFALL	TEMP	
3	Months	(cms)	(C)	
4	January	1.8	22	
5	February	1.8	22	
6	March	2.5	22	
7	April	4.0	21	
8	May	7.0	17	
9	June	8.0	12	
10	July	7.0	11	
11	August	6.0	11	
12	September	5.0	13	
13	October	4.5	16	
14	November	3.0	18	
15	December	2.5	21	
16				

4. Save the workbook as **Adelaide**.

5. Re-save the workbook as a **text file**, named **Adelaide Weather**.

6. Close the workbook.

7. Open **Adelaide** again and save it as a template named **Adelaide Template**, so it could be used again.

8. Close the workbook.

16. Formulas

These exercises include topics taken from the following list: creating formulas, using brackets, **AutoSum** and checking for errors.

Exercise 4.7

1. On a blank worksheet enter the numbers in the cells to match below.

	A	B	C	D	E
1	**Course Attendances**				
2					
3		**Term1**	**Term 2**	**Term 3**	**Total**
4	Spanish	20	12	5	
5	Pottery	8	9	7	
6	Yoga	15	18	16	
7	Self Defence	6	11	16	
8	All Courses				
9					

2. Click in cell **B8**. Use a formula to add the four cells above. What is the total?

3. Click in cell **E4**. Click the **AutoSum** button. Press <**Enter**>. What is the answer?

4. Complete cells **C8**, **D8**, **E5**, **E6** and **E7**.

5. Click in cell **E8**. **AutoSum** is to be used to sum the column or the row of totals. Click the **AutoSum** button and press <**Enter**>. Does it sum the column or the row? What is the answer?

6. Delete the contents of **E8**. Use **AutoSum** again but click and drag to select the row of numbers, **B8:D8**. Is it the same answer as before?

7. Save the workbook as **Courses**.

8. In cell **B9** enter the formula **=B8/total**. What error value is shown and why?

9. Change the formula in **B9** to be **=B8/E8**. It should now give a valid result.

10. Use the <**Delete**> key to clear the contents of cell **E8**. What error value is shown in **B9** and why?

11. Highlight the whole of column **E** and remove it (do <u>not</u> use the <**Delete**> key). What error value is shown in **B9** and why?

12. Close the workbook <u>without</u> saving.

Exercise 4.8

1. Start a new workbook.

2. Create the following worksheet.

	A	B	C	D	E	F
1	Computer Equipment Sales					
2						
3	Sales	PCs	Printers	Scanners	Modems	Total Units
4	John	9	3	2	3	
5	Natalie	5	5	4	0	
6	Asif	7	2	5	0	
7	Craig	10	1	0	1	
8	Alex	3	7	3	1	
9	Total					
10						

3. Complete row **9** and column **F**, using **AutoSum**.

4. Add the following data to rows **11** and **12**.

10					
11	Profit per Item	50	20	10	5
12	Total Profit				
13					

5. Complete row **12** using a formula to calculate the profit made from selling each item.

6. Sum the row to find the overall profit from selling all the items. What is the profit?

7. Enter the salespersons' names again in **A15:A19**. In cells **B15:B19**, calculate the profit made by each salesperson. Who made the most profit for the company?

8. Check all the formulas by double clicking on each in turn.

9. Save the completed workbook as **Computer Sales** and then close it.

10. Why is it better to use cell references in formulas, rather than typing in numbers?

17. *Workbooks*

These exercises include topics taken from the following list: using multiple sheets, switching between sheets, renaming, copying, moving, inserting and deleting sheets.

Exercise 4.9

1. Open the workbook **Forecast**. This workbook compares an estimate of sales for a three month period against the actual sales. The comparison is shown on the chart worksheet.

2. Display the **Chart** worksheet. How would you describe the attempt at estimating the sales figures: a) within 1000 either way - good, b) more than 1000 over - too optimistic, c) more than 1000 under - too pessimistic.

3. Delete the **Chart** sheet.

4. Copy the **Estimate** sheet to a new workbook.

5. Save the workbook as **Copy** and leave it open.

6. Switch to the **Forecast** workbook and insert a new sheet ready to add more detailed information.

7. Which is better when naming worksheets: to use the default name, e.g. **Sheet1**, or to change the name?

8. Rename the new sheet **Accounts**.

9. Move the **Accounts** sheet to be the first sheet in the book.

10. Select the entire worksheet and change the font to **Tahoma**.

11. Save the workbook as **Forecast2**.

12. Close the workbook and close the **Copy** workbook.

Exercise 4.10

1. Open the workbook **Divisions**. This is a workbook that contains six worksheets, each representing a division within a company.

2. Rename **Sheet1** as **North**.

3. Rename **Sheet2** as **Midlands**. Rename all the other sheets with the name of the **Division** contained in cell **B9** of each worksheet.

4. Move the **Midlands** sheet to between **South** and **East**.

5. Move the **South West** sheet to between **North** and **South** as shown.

6. Delete the **Midlands** sheet.

7. The company has opened another division. Copy the **South West** worksheet to create a new division sheet to be located before the **South** sheet.

8. Rename the new worksheet as **South East**.

9. Enter the label **South East** in cell **B9**.

10. Save the workbook as **Divisions2**.

11. Close the workbook.

18. Editing

These exercises include topics taken from the following list: editing and deleting cell content, using undo and redo, using the fill handle, copying and moving cells, finding specific text and replacing text.

Exercise 4.11

1. Open the workbook **Petty Cash**.

2. In cell **E5** enter the formula **=E4-D5** to reduce the **Total** by the amount spent.

3. Copy this formula down the column to cell **E13**.

4. Calculate the difference in cell **E17** between the reducing total and the cash as counted.

5. The difference is not **0**. What is it?

6. After checking the receipts you find that the **Coffee** was **5.50** not **5.00**. Use the search feature to find the entry for coffee and make the change.

7. A receipt was found that had been missed. Add the details **25** of the month, **Office** expense for **Milk** at **12.65**.

8. Copy the formula to **E14** to calculate the **Total**.

9. Adjust the formula in cell **E17**. What is the **Difference** now?

10. The last receipt should be **Miscellaneous**. Copy and paste to make the change.

11. Save the workbook as **Petty Cash Sept**.

12. Copy all the data and paste it into a new workbook. Change the title to **Petty Cash for Oct 2009** and save as **Petty Cash Oct**.

13. Cut all the data from **Petty Cash Oct** and paste it into a new workbook, this time changing the title to **Petty Cash for Nov** and saving the workbook as **Petty Cash Nov**.

14. Close the workbook and close **Petty Cash Sept**. Close **Petty Cash Oct** without saving.

Exercise 4.12

1. Open the workbook **Lists**. This contains a worksheet with three blocks of data: **Names**, **Numbers** and **Alphanumerics**.

2. Leave the original columns as they are, highlight each of the other lists in turn and sort the data according to the labels at the top of each column.

3. Which number comes first in ascending order?

4. Which name comes last in descending order?

5. To compare the three different types of data, copy the three original blocks to form a new continuous column starting in cell **B15**.

6. Sort the new block into ascending order.

7. What type of data comes first?

8. Undo the sort and resort in descending order.

9. With the column still selected, replace all occurrences of **j** with **a**. How many replacements?

10. Re-sort the list in ascending order.

11. Which item is 10th in the list?

12. Experiment with another block of data to determine if upper and lowercase letters have any effect after being sorted.

13. Close the workbook <u>without</u> saving.

19. Printing

These exercises include topics taken from the following list: printing, print preview and page setup, changing margins, adding headers and footers, printing part of a worksheet, adding print titles, setting print options and displaying and printing formulas.

Exercise 4.13

1. Open the workbook **Income**.

2. **Print Preview** the worksheet (using **Print** in *Excel 2010/2013*).

3. In **Page Setup**, add the **filename** field in the centre section of the header.

4. Add fields for the worksheet name and the date and time into the left and right of the footer respectively.

5. Change the page orientation to **Landscape**.

6. Select to fit to one page.

7. Reduce the left, right, top and bottom margins to **0.5**.

8. Display the formulas.

9. Adjust the columns to display the full contents of every cell.

10. Choose to print the gridlines and the row and column headings. Make sure that any new pages will have titles printed.

11. Print a copy of the worksheet.

12. Turn off the formulas, gridlines and row and column headings.

13. Obtain a printout of Jan- March and May only, i.e. the ranges **A1:D16** and **F1:F16** by selecting the range of non-adjacent cells.

14. Close the workbook <u>without</u> saving.

Exercise 4.14

1. Open the workbook **Grand Hotel**.

2. **Print Preview** the spreadsheet (using **Print** in *Excel 2010/2013*). How many pages are there?

3. Alter the page setup to print the worksheet in **Landscape** with **row 1** repeated at the top of every page. Change the left and right margins to **0.9cm**.

4. Print the first 2 pages.

5. Select to fit the print to one page and preview the result.

6. Cancel the fit option and set the print scaling to **80%**.

7. Remove the footer.

8. The hotel manager is about to start a cost cutting exercise, print out only the details of payments, including the months as titles.

9. The accountant wants to check the formulas for the first six months of the year. Display the formulas, gridlines and row and column headings. Print out the required part.

10. Remove the formulas and switch off the printed gridlines and row and column headings.

11. **Print Preview** the worksheet to check for the normal display.

12. Close the workbook <u>without</u> saving.

20. Formatting

These exercises include topics taken from the following list: adding bold, underline and italic, changing font and font size, formatting numbers and dates, cell alignment, changing row height and column width, inserting and deleting rows and columns, adding borders and colour, rotating cell content, freezing panes and using zoom.

Exercise 4.15

1. Open the workbook **Theatre**. This workbook compares theatre audiences for a specific week for several large cities. Insert a new row **2**.

2. Freeze panes so that row **3** and above will always remain in view when the screen is scrolled down. Widen column **A** to display the day labels in full.

3. Insert a new column before column **G** and in **G3** enter **Paris**. Enter the figures for the week as **1750**, **1600**, **1500**, **1550**, **1800** and **1850**.

4. Adjust columns **B** to **G** to **AutoFit** the data in those columns.

5. Sum the columns and the rows.

6. What was the total attendance for the whole week for all the cities?

7. Which city has the largest attendance for the week?

8. Which day was the most popular?

9. Rotate the text in the range **B3:H3** to **45** degrees.

10. Remove the italic formatting from the range **A4:A9** and underline the city names.

11. Change the height of row **9** to **21.00** units.

12. Change the width of columns **B:H** to **8.00** units.

13. Add dashed borders (**Outline** and **Inside**) and a **light yellow** background to the range **A3:H10**.

14. Change the cell colour of the range **B4:G9** to **light blue** and change the underlined city names to double underlined.

15. In cell **A1** increase the font size to **14pt**.

16. Enter your first name in cell **B12** and the date in cell **C12**, date style **--/--/--**. Format the range **B4:G9** as number, 0 decimal places and use the thousand separator.

17. Save the workbook as **Theatre2** and close it.

Exercise 4.16

1. Open the workbook **Market Stall**.

2. Change the font size of the title in **A1** to **16pt** and make it **bold**. Merge and centre the title into row **A**.

3. Freeze column **A**. Scroll to the right to check that column **A** stays on the screen.

4. Format the ranges **B3:N12** and **B14:N15** as currency, no decimal places but include the currency symbol.

5. Format the range **B15:N15** to display negative values in red with a negative sign.

6. Change the width of column **A** to **16.00** units (**117 pixels**).

7. Align the data in the range **A3:A15** horizontally and vertically.

8. Using zoom, fit the entire worksheet on the screen.

9. **Print Preview** the worksheet. What is the orientation and how many pages are there?

10. Change the setup of the worksheet to display it best on one piece of paper.

11. Select rows **2** and **15** and fill with pale green. Select the columns **Feb**, **Apr**, **Jun**, **Aug**, **Oct** and **Dec** and fill with the same green.

12. Save the workbook as **Market Stall Formatted**.

13. Unfreeze column **A**.

14. Close the workbook.

21. Functions and Addressing

These exercises include topics taken from the following list: using sum, count, average, maximum, minimum, IF and applying relative, absolute and mixed addressing.

Exercise 4.17

1. Start a new workbook and create the worksheet below (shown overleaf).

	A	B	C	D
1	Stationery Sales 1st Quarter			
2				
3		Sold	Price	Sales
4	Pens	456	5.68	
5	A4 Paper	345	3.25	
6	Calculators	23	8.99	
7	Box Files	665	4.99	
8	Pencils	345	0.23	
9	Rulers	89	1.69	
10	Total Sold		Total Sales	
11				

2. **Embolden** the title cells **A1**, **A10** and **C10**.

3. **Right** align and make **bold** the range **B3:D3** and cell **C10**.

4. Complete the **Sales** column by multiplying the number **Sold** by **Price**.

5. Use **AutoSum** to total the **Sales** column.

6. **Centre** the title in cell **A1** across columns **A** to **D**.

7. Increase the font size of the title to **14pt**.

8. In cell **C13** enter the label **Average**.

9. In cell **D13** calculate the average of the range **D4:D9**.

10. Format cell **D13** to display two decimal places. What is the average value of sales?

11. In cell **E13**, use the **round** function to convert the average value to **0** decimal places.

12. In cell **C14** enter the label **Highest**.

13. Use a function to display the highest sales.

14. In cell **C15** enter the label **Lowest**.

15. Use a function to display the lowest sales

16. In cell **E3** enter the label **Average +/-**. Widen the column to display all the text.

17. In cell **E4** enter a formula to calculate the difference between the sales and the average in cell **D13**. To be able to copy this formula down the row, edit the formula to fix cell **D13**.

18. Copy the formula down the column.

19. In cell **E10 AutoSum** the column to check that the calculations are correct. The total should be **0**.

20. Delete the content of **E13** then save the workbook as **Stationery Sales**.

21. Close the workbook.

Exercise 4.18

1. Open the **Results** workbook. This worksheet records the percentage scores from tests taken.

2. Double click in cell **A1** and add your name to the end of the text.

3. In cell **A22** enter the label **Average Mark**.

4. In cell **B22** calculate the average of the marks using a function. What is the average?

5. You were absent for the **Chemistry** test through illness. Delete the **0** in cell **B12**. This increases your average as blank cells are not counted. What is the average now?

6. In cell **A23** enter the label **Number of Subjects**. Replace the **0** in cell **B12**.

7. In cell **B23** calculate the number of subjects. The number of subjects is calculated using the **COUNT** function (remember to count the marks, not the subject titles).

8. Delete the function in cell **B23** and replace it with the **COUNTBLANK** function. Because cell **B12** contains a 0, the result shows **0** as the result, as with the **COUNT** function.

9. Delete the **0** in cell **B12** and check the result; it now shows **1**, i.e. 1 blank cell. Replace the **0** and change the function to **COUNTA**. This gives the same result as **COUNT**.

10. Add **Highest Mark** in cell **A24** and **Lowest Mark** in cell **A25**.

11. Enter functions in cells **B24** and **B25** to calculate the highest and lowest marks.

12. Enter the label **Pass/Fail** in cell **C3**.

13. Use the **Format Painter** to copy the formats from **B3** to **C3**.

14. The pass rate for each of these examinations is **50** marks. Use the **IF** function in cell **C4** to display **Pass** for marks over **49** and **Fail** for marks **49** and under.

15. Right align the contents of cell **C4**.

16. Copy this formula using the **Fill Handle** down the column to cell **C20**. How many tests resulted in a **Pass**?

17. Print a copy of the worksheet.

18. Save the workbook as **Results2** then close it.

22. Charts

These exercises include topics taken from the following list: creating charts, embedded charts, changing chart type, formatting and printing charts.

Exercise 4.19

1. Open the workbook **TV**. This contains a breakdown of TV viewing figures.

2. Increase the font size of the text in cell **A1** to **14pt**.

3. Increase the height of rows **3** to **8** to **18.00 units**.

4. Format cell **C3** to wrap the text. Why does cell **C3** not adjust to display all the text?

5. Adjust the height of row **3** to display the label in cell **C3** in full. Right align **C3**.

6. Rename the sheet as **Data**.

7. Highlight the range **B3:C8** and create a **Pie Chart with a 3-D visual effect**.

8. On the **Titles** tab, add the title **TV Viewing Figures**.

9. Remove the **Legend**, but add the **Category name** and **Value** to the **Pie Chart**.

10. Create the **Pie Chart** on the same sheet as the data. Move the chart so that it is under the data.

11. Format the chart title as follows: edit the text to **Viewing Figures**, change the font size to **16pt**, add a **pale yellow** background and add an automatic border.

12. Change the colours of each piece of pie as desired and reduce the size of the chart by about a third.

13. Explode the **Channel2** segment, and then print a copy of the worksheet.

14. Save the workbook as **Chart** and then close it.

Exercise 4.20

1. Open the workbook **Temperatures**.

2. Complete row **17**, the average temperatures.

3. Format the range **B17:F17** to display one decimal place.

4. Which city has the highest average temperature and what is it?

5. Chart the temperatures of **London** and **Toronto** as **Clustered Columns**.

6. Add the chart options, Title **Temperatures**, X axis title **Months**, Y axis title **Temps**. Leave the **Legend** displayed on the right.

7. Create the chart on a separate sheet, named **Chart**.

8. Move the **Chart** worksheet to the right of the **Temperatures** worksheet.

9. Remove the colour from the plot area and fill the legend with pale blue. Change the font of the legend to **Tahoma 9pt** and the colour of the text to dark blue.

10. Change the fill effect of the **Toronto** series to a pattern or a texture that would help to distinguish the two sets of data when printed in black and white.

11. Print a copy of the chart.

12. Remove the chart title and change the chart type to a bar chart. Now change the chart type to a line chart.

13. Print a copy of the chart and then delete it.

14. Undo the deletion.

15. In general, how would you describe the relative temperatures in the two cities based on the two series on this chart?

16. Save the workbook as **Temperature Chart** and close it.

Spreadsheet Software General Exercises

The following revision exercises can involve processes from any part of the ECDL module *Spreadsheet Software*.

Exercise 4.21

1. Start a new workbook and save it as **Dogs**.

2. Open the workbook **Dog Show** and cut the entire worksheet; paste this data into the **Dogs** workbook and close the **Dog Show** workbook <u>without</u> saving.

3. Insert a new column, **Pet Name**, between **Dog KC Name** and **Breed** and enter the following details down the column: **Paddy**, **Beau**, **Milly**, **Buster**, **Suzy**, **Coco**, **Poppy**, **Cherie**, **Cashew** and **Sam**.

4. Insert a new row **9** and enter the following details: **Lord Charlie of Sandwell**, **Sandy**, **English Bull Terrier**, best rank **1**, ranked **1** in **2008**. This is the only year in which this dog ranked.

5. There is an error in the information. Poppy is a **Dalmatian**, not a **Doberman**. Use the **Find and Replace** feature to correct the error.

6. How many of the dogs are **Labradors**? Use search to find out.

7. Format the headings with a double underline and change the orientation of this cell content to 45 degrees.

8. Undo this formatting. Format **Dog KC Name** as italic, underlined and blue. Copy this formatting to the other headings.

9. The details for rankings in 2005 are no longer needed. Delete the column.

10. In cell **D15** enter the title **Total Rankings** and in **F15** use the **COUNT** function to show the number of rankings obtained in 2006 for this group of dogs.

11. In cell **G15** use **COUNTA** to do the same for 2007. Copy the function to **H15**.

12. In cell **I15**, use the **COUNTBLANK** function to see how many dogs <u>didn't</u> rank in 2009. Format the cell contents as **Italic** and **Underlined**.

13. Create a column chart on a new sheet named **Show Chart** using the information in columns **C** and **E** only. Enter the value Y axis title as **Rank**.

14. Change the chart to a bar chart and change the colours of the bars to red. Delete the chart title and change the formatting of all remaining text to **Arial bold 9pt**.

15. Print 2 copies of the chart and then delete it.

16. Rename **Sheet1** as **Show Results** sheet and ensure that it is set up to automatically print title rows on each page.

17. In the header, enter the file name at the left as a field, the date as a field in the centre and your full name at the right. In the footer, add centred page numbers as a field. Adjust the orientation to landscape.

18. Print the range **D2:I15**.

19. Save and close the workbook.

Exercise 4.22

1. Start *Excel* and check the **User name** in **Options**. Enter your name if it is not already set.

2. Open the workbook **Cottages**. This workbook contains information about a property company buying, selling and letting holiday cottages. On the **Cashflow** worksheet, widen column **A** to display the data in full, ensuring only 1 element of data is in each cell.

3. Increase the font size in cell **A1** to **12pt** and make the text bold. Increase the height of rows **1** to **14** to **18.00** units and right align the labels in the range **B1:M1**.

4. Add a single border line to the bottom of the range **A1:N1**, and a top and bottom line to the ranges, **A4:N4** and **A12:N12**.

5. In late February wind blew the roof off four cottages. The **Repairs and Maintenance** costs were **1,700** for **February** and **5,000** for **March**; make the changes.

6. Use a formula to add together the cells **B2** and **B3** in cell **B4**. Copy the formula in cell **B4** to the range **C4:N4**.

7. Enter a function in cell **B12** to calculate the total for the range **B5:B11**. Copy the function in cell **B12** to the range **C12:N12**.

8. To calculate the **Profit** in cell **B13**, subtract the contents of cell **B12** from the contents of **B4** and then copy the formula to the range **C13:N13**.

9. The cumulative profit for January in cell **B14** is simply a copy of the cell above - enter the formula **=B13**.

10. The February cumulative profit in cell **C14** is the January figure plus February's profit, i.e. **=B14+C13**; enter this formula. Copy this formula in cell **C14** to the range **D14:M14**.

11. The **Total Cumulative Profit** in cell **N14** is the same as for **December** in cell **M14**. Enter the formula.

12. Freeze the titles in column **A** so that the labels are always in view.

13. In cell **M17** add the text **Percentage Profit**. **Right** align the data in the cell.

14. Calculate the **Profit** as a percentage of the **Turnover** (cell **N13** divided by cell **N4**) in cell **N17**. Format the percentage in cell **N17** to one decimal place. What is it?

15. Insert the text **Cashflow for Holiday Cottages** into the header of the **Cashflow** worksheet. Change the orientation of the worksheet to landscape and make sure it prints on one page only. Print a copy of the **Cashflow** worksheet.

16. Using the **Lettings** worksheet, create a line chart from the range **A3:B15**, placed on the worksheet with the data, with the chart title **Lettings**.

17. Move the chart up and to the right of the data. Resize the embedded chart until the names of all of the months across the **x** axis are displayed.

18. Save the workbook as **Holiday Cottages** then resave it as a template named **Cottage Template**.

19. Close the workbook and close *Excel*.

Exercise 4.23

1. Open the workbook **Wines**. This workbook contains information about a small wine shop.

2. Use help to find out how to widen columns, then on the **Wines** worksheet, adjust the width of column **A** to display the data fully.

3. Change the font colour of the range **A3:G3** to **blue**. Make the contents of cell **A1** **bold**.

4. Cell **F3** contains a large label for a column of small numbers; wrap the text in cell **F3**. **Right** align the labels in the range **E3:G3**.

5. Change the **zoom** to **90%** and in cell **G4**, complete the formula to determine the value of the wine by multiplying cell **E4** by cell **F4** (price x stock level). Copy this formula to the range **G5:G25**.

6. Format the range **G4:G25** to display as currency with the appropriate symbol and two decimal places. The manager has decided to reduce the price of two wines to make them wines of the month. Change the **W05** price to **6.59** and the **R10** to **7.99**.

7. After stock taking, two of the levels were found to be incorrect; adjust the stock levels of **R04** to **80** and **W08** to **59**. Sort the range **A3:G25** by **Name** in ascending order.

8. Calculate the total cost of the wine in stock in cell **G26** using an appropriate function. Add a cell border of a single top line and double bottom line to cell **G26**.

9. Adjust the height of row **26** to **18** units.

10. On the **Sales** worksheet, correct the error in the formula in cell **F26**. In cell **A28**, enter the label **Highest** and use a function to calculate the highest number in the range **B4:B25** (**Week1**).

11. In cell **A29**, enter the label **Lowest** and use a function to calculate the lowest number in the range **B4:B25**.

12. In cell **A30**, enter the label **Average** and use a function to calculate the average number of the sales in the range **B4:B25**. Format cell **A30** as a number with no decimal places.

13. Copy these three functions across the next **4** columns. What is the best selling wine in the whole four week period?

14. On the **Sales** worksheet move the contents of cell **A1** to **A3**. Delete the unnecessary blank rows **1** and **2**.

15. Highlight the two ranges **A1:A23** and **F1:F23** to create a clustered column chart of the wine sales. Amend the chart title to **Total Sales** and remove the **Legend**. Create the chart as an object on the **Sales** worksheet.

16. Move the chart to the right of the data and resize it to display all of the x axis labels. Remove the **Plot Area** colour.

17. Click away from the chart and change the **Page Setup** to display the worksheet in **Landscape** with left and right margins as **0.5cm** and a centred header - **Sales Week1 to Week4**. Add your name in the left section of the footer and scale the worksheet to fit on one page.

18. Print a single copy of the **Sales** worksheet displaying the data and the chart.

19. Save the current position of the workbook using the file name **Wine Warehouse** and then close it.

Exercise 4.24

1. Open the workbook **Tournament**. This workbook contains information and the results of a Tenpin Bowling competition. The handicap column is a number that is added to each game score to try and level different abilities.

2. **Centre** align the range **E4:E31**. Change the font in cell **A1** to **Times New Roman** and the font size to **16pt**. Rename **Sheet1** as **Entries**. In cell **D32** use an appropriate function to total all the entry fees.

3. Two people have not turned up for the tournament; delete the rows where the **Registered** column contains **N**. In cell **C32** enter the label **Entries** and in cell **D32** use a function to determine the number of bowlers. How many entries are there?

4. Note the amount of fees collected. Display **Sheet3** and enter the amount of fees in cell **C5**. Rename **Sheet3** as **Accounts**.

5. Calculate the total income in cell **C6** using a simple formula to add the cells. Use an appropriate function in cell **C15** to total the range **C9:C14**.

6. In cell **B19**, enter the text **Prize Fund** and in cell **C19** use a formula to find the difference in total income (cell **C6**) and total expenditure (cell **C15**). What is the value of the prize fund?

7. This fund is to be shared in the following way: half to the winner, a third to the second and a sixth to the third. In cell **C21** enter a formula to divide the prize fund by **2**, in cell **C22** enter a formula to divide the prize fund by **3** and in cell **C23** enter a formula to divide the prize fund by **6**.

8. Note the three values and enter them in the range **C10:C12** (be careful as the calculated values will change reducing to **0** when complete). The total income and total expenditure should now be the same. The calculations are no longer needed. Delete the range **B19:C23**.

9. On the **Accounts** worksheet, create a standard **Pie chart** of the expenditure range, **B9:C14**. Include the chart title **Breakdown of Expenditure** and add percentages as **Data Labels**. What percentage of the expenses is the **First Place** prize money?

10. Display **Sheet2**. Rename the sheet **Results**. Format the labels **K3:L3** to wrap the text. **Right** align the range **D3:L3**.

11. Display the **Entries** sheet and copy the range **A4:C29** to the **Results** sheet, starting in cell **A4**. Widen column **A** to display the names in full.

12. Open the workbook **Bowling Scores**. Copy the range **B5:G30**. Switch back to the **Tournament** workbook and paste the range to the **Results** worksheet, starting in cell **D4**.

13. On the **Results** worksheet in cell **J4** total the six games, i.e. **D4:I4**. Copy this formula to the range **J5:J29**.

14. In cell **K4** enter a formula to calculate the **Total Handicap**, which is the contents of cell **C4** multiplied by **6**. Copy this formula to the range **K5:K29**.

15. Add the **Total** and the **Handicap Total** in cell **L4**. Copy this formula to the range **L5:L29**. The results are now complete; sort the block of data, descending, using column **L** the **Grand Total**. The winners are at the top of the list.

16. Insert a new worksheet. Rename the new worksheet **Roll of Honour**. On this worksheet, list the 1st 2nd and 3rd prize winners with their winnings. Format the list appropriately.

17. Display the **Results** worksheet. There is a prize for the highest score for each game. Use a function at the bottom of each **Game** column to display the highest score.

18. Locate the winning names for each of the six games and transfer them to the **Roll of Honour** worksheet. The prize for each high game is **25**.

19. Save the workbook as **Tournament Results** and close it. Close the **Bowling Scores** workbook.

Exercise 4.25

1. Open the workbook **World Cup**. This includes attendance, a league table and income for a major world sporting event held in Canada.

2. On the **Attendance** worksheet in cell **A9** enter your country. Copy cell **A9** and paste to cell **A6** in the **Table** worksheet.

3. In the **Attendance** worksheet, format the cell **A1** to be **bold**, **blue** font colour, font size **16pt** and the font **Times New Roman**.

4. Add a single border to the bottom of the range of cells, **A6:D6**. Format the range **B6:D6** to be **right** aligned and wrap the text of the labels.

5. In cell **D7**, calculate the stadium **Usage** by dividing the **Average Attendance** in cell **B7** by the **Stadium Capacity** in cell **C7**. Copy the formula to the range **D8:D13**.

6. Format the range **D7:D13** as percentages with one decimal place.

7. Create a **3-D Clustered column chart** of the **Average Attendances** using the range **A6:B13**. Leave the chart title as **Average Attendance** but remove the **Legend**. Add the chart to the **Attendance** worksheet.

8. Move the chart to below the data, to the left. Resize the chart to display all of the **Team** names.

9. Using **Page Setup**, select to print the worksheet on one sheet of paper. Add your name to the left section of the footer and type today's date (not as a code) in the right section of the footer. Select to print the **Gridlines** and the **Row and column headings**.

10. Print one copy of the **Attendance** worksheet.

11. Display the **Income** worksheet. In cell **C20** use an appropriate function to calculate the total number of **Seats Sold**.

12. In cell **D13** calculate, using a formula, the value of the **Lower Tier Ends** seats by multiplying cell **B13** by cell **C13**. Copy this formula to the range **D14:D19**.

13. Complete the **Total Value** in cell **D20**.

14. In cell **B5** add a formula to copy the value in cell **D20** and divide it by **1000**. Display the result as a number with no decimal places. In cell **B8** total the income for the game.

15. Display the **Table** worksheet. This is a league table of the matches played.

16. Wrap the text in the range **B3:H3**. Adjust the width of the columns **B** to **I** to **9 units**.

17. Place the cursor inside the table and sort it in descending order by points.

18. Move the **Table** worksheet to the left of the **Income** worksheet and save the workbook as **World Cup2**.

19. Save again as a text file named **World Cup Text** and close it.

Exercise 4.26

1. Open the workbook **Fish**. This workbook contains information on tropical fish, fish tanks and associated costs. Save the workbook as **Tropical Fish**.

2. On the **Tank** worksheet, in cell **E4** enter the formula that calculates the volume of the first tank in litres. Multiply the length, width and height of the tank and then divide by **1000**.

3. Copy the formula to the range **E5:E17**. Format the range **E4:E17** to display the values as numbers to one decimal place.

4. Having completed some background reading, you have decided to buy a tank that holds at least 40 litres of water. Enter **40** in cell **E19**. Increase the height of row **19** to **16.50** units.

5. In cell **G4** enter a function that compares the amount in **E4** with the required amount in cell **E19** (make **E19** an absolute reference to be able to copy down the column). If the tank is not big enough, display **Too small**, otherwise display **OK** (remember to add the speech marks around the text).

6. Copy this function to the range **E5:E17**. You decide to get a bigger tank to offer you more scope. Change the value in cell **E19** to **50**.

7. The tanks are listed in order of tank length. What is the smallest length of tank that matches the requirement?

8. How many of the **14** tanks are **Too small**?

9. Display the **Costs** worksheet and right align the range **A4:G4**.

10. Using an appropriate function, total the costs for **Tank 1**. What is the cost? Copy this function to the range **G6:G18**.

11. Your budget for a tank is **200**. Which tank is the biggest (length) that you can afford? Check the measurements of your chosen tank on the **Tank** worksheet, then display the **Fish** worksheet. Name the fish that would be unsuitable for your tank.

12. Sort the list into alphabetical order using the fish names. Insert a new worksheet. Rename the worksheet **Shopping List**.

13. Copy the range **A3:E3** from the **Tank** worksheet to starting cell **B3** on the **Shopping List** worksheet. Copy the range of your chosen **Tank** to starting cell **B4** on the **Shopping List** worksheet.

14. Copy the range **A4:G4** from the **Costs** worksheet to the **Shopping List** worksheet starting on cell **B7**.

15. Copy the range of the costs for your chosen **Tank** on the **Costs** worksheet to the **Shopping List** worksheet starting on cell **B8**. Widen any columns as necessary to display all the data.

16. Enter the label **Shopping List** in cell **B1**. Format the cell contents to be **14pt**, **Bold** and font colour **blue**. Merge and centre the label in cell **B1** to the range **B1:H1**.

17. On the **Shopping List** worksheet, create a **Pie** chart of the range **C7:G8**. Add a chart title **Cost of Tropical Fish Tank** and remove the **Legend**, Add **Data Labels** to include **Category name** and **Percentage** value for each segment.

18. Create the chart with the data. Move the chart to start at column **B**, under the data. What **Percentage** of the cost involved is for the actual tank?

19. Click away from the chart and print preview the worksheet.

20. Add a customised footer with your name in the centre section and today's date in the right section.

21. Print a copy of the worksheet and save the workbook using the same name.

22. Display the **Tank** worksheet and delete the contents of cell **E19**.

23. Save the workbook using the existing name.

24. Save the workbook again, this time as a template using the same name.

25. Close the workbook and close *Excel*.

Database Software Section Exercises

The following revision exercises are divided into sections, each targeted at specific elements of the ECDL module *Database Software*. The individual sections are an exact match for the sections in the ECDL training guides from CiA Training, making the guides an ideal reference source for anyone working through these exercises.

23. Databases

These exercises include topics taken from the following list: key concepts, starting *Access*, screen layout, help, opening databases and tables, closing databases and tables.

Exercise 5.1

1. What is a database?

2. What is the difference between **data** and **information**?

3. List some common uses of large scale databases.

4. How is a database organised?

5. Open *Access*.

6. Open the database **Fixit** from the supplied data files. Make sure the database window is <u>not</u> maximised.

7. How many tables are in the database and what are their names?

8. Display the contents of one of the tables.

9. Use the **Help** feature to find information on **expression builder**. According to *Microsoft* **Help**, what are the three component boxes of the **Expression Builder** dialog box called?

10. What is the **ToolTip** shown for the following buttons on the toolbar or **Home** tab?

          a)   b)

11. Find how many **Macros** are defined in this database.

12. What would be the effect of clicking the **Close** button in the very top right corner of the screen?

    a)   The database will close but *Access* will stay open.

    b)   *Access* will close but the database will stay open.

    c)   Both *Access* and the database will close.

13. Close the database then close *Access*.

Exercise 5.2

1. What does a database specialist do?

2. What tasks do normal **database users** perform?

3. What tasks does a **database administrator** perform? What are their responsibilities?

4. Open *Access*.

5. Open the database **Central** from the supplied data files.

6. Open the **Premises** table in **Datasheet** view. This shows a list of commercial properties for sale by the Central City Properties Company.

7. How many records are in this table? How can you find this out without counting all the records?

8. How many fields does each record have?

9. What is the address for the record with a **Premises ID** of **P002**?

10. Close the **Premises** table. There should be no prompt to save changes. Which of the following actions would require the table to be saved before closing?

    a   Changing the data in a field.

    b   Adding a new record.

    c   Adding a new field.

    d   Changing a column width.

11. Close the **Central** database.

24. Tables

These exercises include topics taken from the following list: database organisation, creating databases and tables, formatting and editing field properties, defining primary keys, creating index fields, entering data, creating validation rules and printing tables.

Exercise 5.3

1. Is it okay for a table to contain data relating to lots of subjects?

2. What must you consider when changing data types or field properties?

3. Create a new blank database called **Learning** to be saved in the folder with the supplied data files.

4. Create a new table with the following structure, adding appropriate validation text where necessary.

Field Name	Data Type	Properties	Validation Rule?
Course ID	Number	Integer	No
Description	Text	Length 50	No
Tutor	Text	Length 20	No
Basic Cost	Currency	0 decimal places	Must be no more than 200
Funding	Yes/No	Default value No	No

5. The **Course ID** is always a six character field which contains letters and numbers. Change the data type and properties accordingly. What have you changed?

6. Before saving the table, define **Course ID** as the primary key. What is the main criterion for a suitable primary key field?

7. Save the table as **Courses**.

8. Add another 20 character text field called **Location** to the table design, to appear between the **Tutor** and **Basic Cost** fields.

9. Add a validation rule to the **Location** field, so that only entries of **Main**, **Annexe** or **Riverside** will be allowed.

10. Create validation text to list the allowed values if an error is made.

11. Save the table and add the following 3 records. Make sure all data is fully displayed.

Course ID	Description	Tutor	Location	Basic Cost	Funding
PH0001	Nuclear Physics	Mr Fletcher	Main	150	Yes
PH0003	Astronomy	Ms Starr	Main	100	No
CH0004	Basic Chemistry	Mr Raman	Annexe	125	No

12. Close the table and re-open it. Which is the first record in the table? Why?

13. Obtain a print of the table in portrait orientation.

14. Close the table.

15. Delete the **Courses** table and close the database.

Exercise 5.4

1. How many elements of data should each field in a table contain?

2. Create a new blank database called **Hotel** to be saved in the folder with the supplied data files.

3. Use the following data to create a blank table. Check In date must be after today.

Field Name	Data Type	Properties	Validation Rule?
Guest Name	Text	Length 30	No
Room No	Number	Integer	Between 05 and 25
Check In	Date/Time	Short Date	> = Now()

4. Save the table as **Register** and let *Access* create a primary key field. What is the name and type of the field *Access* creates?

5. Change the name of the new key field to **Register ID**.

6. Add the following 3 records to the table.

Guest Name	Room No	Check In
Mr Biscuit	21	01/01/2010
Ms Crawley	05	02/06/2010
Mr Banerji	15	02/06/2010

7. Add a new field to the table design as the last field in the table. This field is to hold the number of nights guests will be staying. It is to be called **Nights** and be an **Integer Number** field. Add appropriate data to the table for this extra field.

8. It is decided that the table does not require a primary key. Delete the **Register ID** field. You will need to click **Yes** to all confirmation prompts.

9. An index allows for faster data access. Define the **Room No** field as **Indexed** (no duplicates allowed).

10. Edit the index - duplicates are to be allowed.

11. View the table in **Datasheet View**. In what order are the records displayed?

12. Print a copy of the **Register** table showing only the record for Ms Crawley.

13. Close the **Hotel** database.

25. Table Relationships

These exercises include topics taken from the following list: understanding and applying relationships, creating various types of relationship and applying and understanding referential integrity.

Exercise 5.5

1. What is the main reason for relating tables?

2. Open the **Sunshine** database for the Sunshine Apartments Holidays Company. There are two tables: one for apartment records and one for apartment bookings.

3. The tables need to be linked. Examine each table in **Design** view and identify the field that is common to both tables and is suitable to use as a link field.

4. Use this field to create a link between the tables. If the correct field is used, the link will automatically be shown as a **One To Many** relationship in the dialog box.

5. It is important to maintain the integrity of relationships. Specify **Referential Integrity** (but no **Cascade** options) for the link.

6. Open the **Apartments** table in **Datasheet** view.

7. Display the subdatasheet for unit **B8**. How many bookings have been taken?

8. Open the **Bookings** table in **Datasheet** view and add a booking for unit **B9** for 7 days from today using your name.

9. What error message prevents this? Which database feature has caused this message?

10. Click **OK** at the message then click **Undo** to cancel the input.

11. Close the table and close the **Sunshine** database.

Exercise 5.6

1. How is a relationship built?

2. Open the **Consultants** database, which holds data for a small IT consultancy company. There are tables for staff records, staff costs, and records of staff expenses against projects.

3. Create a **One To Many** relationship between the **Staff** and **Expenses** tables using **Staff No** field as the linking field.

4. Specify **Referential Integrity** for the relationship.

5. After linking the **Staff** and **Expenses** tables, which three of the following statements are true?

    a) A query can include data from **Staff** and **Expenses** tables.

    b) New **Staff** records cannot be added.

    c) **Expenses** records cannot be added for non-existent staff.

    d) Expenses data is available when viewing **Staff** records.

6. Open the **Staff** table in **Datasheet** view.

7. Display the subdatasheet for employee **112**, **Jason Myers**. How many <u>different</u> projects has Jason included in his expense claims?

8. Create a relationship between the **Staff** and **Cost** tables using **Staff No** field as the linking field.

9. What kind of relationship is created? Why is this?

10. Remove the relationship between the **Staff** and **Cost** tables.

11. Close the **Consultants** database.

26. Editing

These exercises include topics taken from the following list: moving and changing width of columns, finding text, using wildcards, editing and deleting data, adding and deleting records and using data entry shortcuts.

Exercise 5.7

1. Open the **Beauty** database.

2. Open the **Bookings** table, showing details of bookings taken for a small beauty salon.

3. The data is not fully displayed. Increase the size of all columns as necessary, so that all data can be seen.

4. Use the **Find** command to find all records with the word **regular** in the **Comment** field. What must the **Match** parameter be set to in order to find the word anywhere within the field? How many records are found?

5. Add a new booking record, reference **1413**, for **Joan Branston**. Use a keyboard shortcut to enter all other values exactly the same as the previous record. What key presses are used? Change the **Time** to **15:00**.

6. **Anna Li** has cancelled her appointment. Delete the record for reference **1407**.

7. Technician **Rose** has left suddenly. Replace her name with **Hortense** in all the relevant records.

8. Close the **Beauty** database.

Exercise 5.8

1. Open the **Club** database.

2. Open the **Membership** table showing details of the club members.

3. Some of the data and column headings are not fully displayed. Widen all necessary columns to rectify this.

4. Change the width of the **Last Name** column to be exactly **20** units. Save the table.

5. Use the **Find** function to find the record for someone living at **Orchard Drive**.

6. This has been entered in error. Change the address for this record to **Apple Drive**.

7. Search for all members who joined on **14/04/2001** and list their names.

8. **Dawn Jenkins** has been dismissed from the club for inappropriate conduct. Find and delete her record.

9. The discount of **5%** has been increased to **7%**. Use find and replace to correct the corresponding records.

10. Add a new record for yourself with the vacant membership number of **FT149**. Use today's date as the **Join Date**, a date next year as the **Next Renewal Date**, **AC** as the **Membership Type**, and no discount.

11. Save the changes to the table and close the **Club** database.

27. Sorting and Filtering

These exercises include topics taken from the following list: sorting data and using filters.

Exercise 5.9

1. Open the **Consultants** database.

2. Open the **Expenses** table.

3. Sort the table in ascending order of **Amount**. What is the cost for the first (lowest value) record?

4. Sort the table to show the most recent record first. What is the date of the first (most recent) record?

5. Using **Filter By Selection**, display all expenses for the **Metro** project. Print the table showing only these records.

6. _Filter Excluding Selection_, display all expenses that are not ... records are found ...

7. Remove the filter. To highlight large e... to show expenses of any type for amounts greater than 1000. How many records are found?

8. Remove the filter. Company policy is that no entertaining expenses can be charged against the **Global** project. Filter the table to show only records for the **Global** project that are for **Entertaining**. What is the staff number of the employee who has broken the rules?

9. Remove all filters and sorts and close the **Consultants** database.

Exercise 5.10

1. Open the **Central** database.

2. Open the **Premises** table and make sure all data and labels are fully displayed.

3. Filter the table to show all premises that are not in **Central Area**. How many records are there?

4. Filter the table to show only premises in the **Riverside Complex**.

5. Sort the filtered list in ascending order of **Price**. What is the address of the cheapest property in the **Riverside Complex**?

6. Similarly, show all the **Office Premises**, regardless of location, in descending order of **Unit Area**. How many records are there and what is the **Premises ID** of the largest one?

7. Remove all filters and sorts.

8. Click a button to apply the filter again. What happens to the data?

9. Remove the filter. Use a filter to find how many unoccupied properties are priced over 100,000.

10. Remove all filters and sorts and close the **Central** database.

28. Queries

These exercises include topics taken from the following list: create, edit and delete a query, use sort in a query, print query results, query related tables, use value ranges, find non-matches and use AND and OR criteria.

Exercise 5.11

1. Open the **Expenses** database. This has details of expense claims for several IT consultants working on a variety of projects.

2. Create a query based on the **Staff** table to show the fields **Staff No**, **Surname**, **Department**, and **Extension**, in that order. Save the query as **Telephone List** and run it.

3. Edit the **Telephone List** query so that the records are shown in alphabetical order of **Surname**, and the **First Name** field is included between **Surname** and **Department**.

4. Use the navigation buttons to select the last record of the query, then the first.

5. Print out the results of the **Telephone List** query in portrait orientation.

6. Create a query based on the **Claims** table to show all the fields for **Miscellaneous** type claims. Save the query as **Check** and run it.

7. Edit the **Check** query so that only miscellaneous claims with a value of greater than **100** are listed and hide the **Expense Type** field from the results.

8. Print out the results of the **Check** query in portrait orientation.

9. Edit the **Check** query again to show subsistence claims with a value of less than 200. Sort the results in descending order by **Amount** and unhide the **Expense Type** field.

10. Print the query results.

11. Now edit the query to show all claims = **582.40**. How many claims are there?

12. The **Check** query may be controversial. Delete it from the database.

13. Create a query based on the **Claims** table, to show all claims that are <u>not</u> for the **Global** project. Show the fields **Date**, **Project Code**, **Expense Type** and **Amount**. Save the query as **Not Global** and print the results.

14. Create a query based on both the **Staff** and **Claims** tables. Show the fields **Surname**, **Department** from **Staff**, and **Project Code**, **Expense Type** and **Amount** from **Claims**. Sort the results alphabetically by **Project Code** and save the query as **Detail**.

15. Print out the results of the **Detail** query in **Landscape** orientation.

16. Close the query and close the **Expenses** database.

Exercise 5.12

1. Open the **Central** database.

2. What is the main purpose of **Queries** within a database?

3. Create a query based on the **Premises** table to show the fields **Premises ID**, **Location**, **Address**, **Type of Premises** and **Price**, in that order. Select only **Store Unit** premises in the **Valley Grove** location. Save the query as **Narrow** and run it.

4. Remove all selection criteria, then select all premises with a **Price** between **100,000** and **200,000**. Save the query as **Mid Range** and run it. Close the query.

5. Open and edit the **Mid Range** query.

6. Remove all selection criteria then select all **Premises** that are not **Store Units**. Save the query as **Non Store** and run it.

7. Edit the **Non Store** query.

8. Remove all selection criteria then add the field **Floors** to the query grid.

9. Select all **Office Premises** with more than a single floor. Save the query as **Floors** and run it.

10. Print a copy of the **Floors** data then delete the query.

11. Use a wildcard to create a query saved as **Units**, showing all fields, which will show any premises that are a type of **Unit**.

12. Sort the query results into ascending order of **Amount**. Print a copy of the query results.

13. Close the **Central** database.

29. Forms

These exercises include topics taken from the following list: Use **AutoForm**, design and create a form, format a form, edit and delete a form, edit data using a form and print from a form.

Exercise 5.13

1. Open the **Club** database.

2. Create a **Columnar AutoForm** (or a **Quick Form** in *2007/2010/2013*) based on the **Membership** table to display and maintain records.

3. Save the form as **Members1**.

4. What is the main use for **Forms** in a database?

5. Use the **Wizard** to create a columnar form including all the fields from the **Membership** table. Select a style, if applicable, and save the form as **Members2**.

6. Create a third form in **Design View**. Include all fields from the **Membership** table and ensure that they are all aligned. Save the form as **Members3**.

7. View each form. **Members2** and **Members3** should be quite similar.

Note: *The example database in the solutions folder assumes that Exercise 5.8 has also been completed. If not, the sequence of fields will be different.*

8. Use the **Members2** form to navigate to the record for member **FT167**, Mr Laurence Lamb.

9. Use the form to change the **Membership Type** for this record to **AM**.

10. Print a copy of the form for this record only.

11. Use a button to display the first record in the table then use the form to delete the record for member **FT167**.

12. Use the **Members2** form to add a new record to the table using the following data:

    Membership Number FT171, Ms Suzi Li, 2 Chester Buildings. Joined on 15/07/2009, next renewal date 01/08/2010. Membership type AM with 20% discount.

13. Print all records.

14. Delete the **Members1** form.

15. Close the **Club** database.

Exercise 5.14

1. Open the **Central** database.

2. Create a columnar form based on the **Premises** table, which has the following layout of fields (as shown overleaf).

Premises ID:	M001	Disabled Access:	Yes
Location:	Valley Grove	Comment:	Recent Acquisition
Address:	Unit 27		
Occupied:	No	Floors:	1
Type of Premises:	Store Unit	Lift:	No
Price:	£50,000.00	Parking Spaces:	35
Unit Area:	78		

3. Save the form as **Properties**.

4. Add a label in the **Form Header** area with the text **Properties Form**.

5. Format the header label as **Arial**, **18pt**, **Bold**.

6. Reduce the height of the **Detail Area** until it is just large enough to include the remaining fields.

7. Print the first page of forms. How many records are shown?

8. Sort the records on the form in ascending order of **Price**.

9. Which **Premises ID** is first?

10. Now sort the records in descending order of **Price**.

11. Which **Premises ID** is first?

12. Sort the records in ascending order by **Address**. Which address is first?

13. Now sort the records in descending order by **Address**. Which address is first?

14. Filter the form to show only locations within the **Enterprise Centre**.

15. How many filtered records are displayed?

16. Remove the filter and close the **Central** database. Do <u>not</u> save the filtered data.

30. Reports and Exporting Data

These exercises include topics taken from the following list: Use **AutoReport**, modify and delete a report, preview and print a report, sort data in a report, group data in a report and perform calculations in a report.

Exercise 5.15

1. Open the **Expenses** database.

2. Create a quick report based on the **Project** table (**Tabular AutoReport** in XP/2003).

3. Save the report as **Project1**.

4. Edit the **Project1** report and change the **Report Header** label to **Project List**.

5. What fields are shown by default in the **Page Footer** area?

6. Add your name as a label so that it will appear once, underneath the last project name on the report. Save and close the report.

7. Use the wizard to create a **Tabular** report based on all fields from the **Staff** table. The records are to be sorted first by **Department**, then by **Surname**, with no grouping. Specify **Landscape** orientation and any style.

8. Save the report as **Staff1**.

9. Edit the **Staff1** report. Change the **Report Header** to **Department Listing** and change the font colour.

10. Delete the **Extension** and **Cost** field from the **Detail** area and their labels from the **Page Header**.

11. Print the first page of the report.

12. Change the paper size to **A5** and print the first page again.

13. Change the paper size back to **A4**.

14. Save the report and close it.

15. Export the **Staff** table in **text file** format as **Staffing** (saving the format) to the location of the data files.

16. Close the **Expenses** database.

Exercise 5.16

1. Open the **Central** database and use the wizard to create a report on the **Premises** table using the following criteria:

    Include only the fields **Premises ID**, **Location**, **Address**, **Type of Premises**, **Occupied** and **Price**.

    Records in the report are to be grouped by **Location** and sorted by **Price**.

    Specify that **Price** is to be summed in a **Detail and Summary** view.

    Specify **Stepped** layout, **Landscape** orientation and **any style** (if required).

2. Save the report as **Location**. Expand any columns necessary to display all data and align the **Summary** field with the detail **Price** field if necessary.

3. What is the cheapest property in **DockLand**?

4. Use the wizard to produce a similar report, but grouped by **Type of Premises** and saved as **Type**. All other criteria will be the same as for the **Location** report.

5. Would you expect the **Grand Total** for each report to be the same? Why?

6. Edit the **Location** report and change the **Report Header** to **Location Analysis**.

7. Swap the **Location Analysis** label with the date (**=Now()**), so that the date is in the **Report Header** area and the label is in the **Page Footer** area. Change the font size of the date field to **18pt** and make sure it is fully displayed.

8. Save the report and close it.

9. Print page 1 of the **Type** report and then delete the report.

10. Create a third report, named **Average**, with all of the same criteria as in steps 1, but **Price** is to be <u>averaged</u> as a **Summary** calculation.

11. Create a query named **Valley**, which shows **Premises ID**, **Address** and **Price**, to display only premises in the location **Valley Grove**. You will need to use the **Location** field in the query but it must be hidden.

12. Export the **Valley** query in **text file** format as **Valley Info**, saving the format, to the data file location. Close the **Central** database.

Database Software
General Exercises

The following revision exercises can involve processes from any part of the ECDL module *Database Software.*

Exercise 5.17

1. The Sunny Vale Campsite had 250 bookings in 2007, 285 in 2008 and 342 in 2009. This is data; what information can be gained from the data?

2. Open *Access*.

3. Create a new, blank database and save it as **Elements**.

4. You've just been informed that a database already exists. Delete the **Elements** database.

5. Open the database **Chemistry** and open the **Elements** table. One of the columns is not wide enough to display the full heading. Widen the appropriate column.

6. Define the **Atomic Number** field as the **Primary Key** for the table. Change the **Field Size** for the **Name** and **Symbol** fields to be **20** characters and **2** characters respectively.

7. Add a validation rule to the **Classification** field so that it will only accept entries of **Metal**, **Solid**, **Liquid** or **Gas**. Set the **Validation Text** to list the allowed values in the event of an invalid entry being made. Add a validation rule to the **Atomic Number** field so that values greater than **100** cannot be entered.

8. Filter the table to show only **Metal** elements. Sort the filtered data in ascending order of **Melting Point**. Print a copy of the filtered table in portrait orientation then remove all filters/sorts.

9. Add a new record to the table for **Krypton** with the values shown below:

Atomic Number	Name	Symbol	Atomic Mass	Melting Point	Boiling Point	Classification
36	Krypton	Kr	84	-157	-153	Gas

10. Create a query to show all fields from those elements classified as gases, sorted in alphabetical order of element name. Save the query as **Gases**.

11. Create another query to show all fields except **Melting Point** and **Boiling Point** to display all elements <u>not</u> classified as gases. Sort the query results in ascending order of **Atomic Mass** and save as **Not Gases**.

12. Print a copy of the **Gases** query and the **Not Gases** query in **Landscape**.

13. Create a query to show **Atomic Number**, **Name**, **Symbol** and **Melting Point** for all elements which melt between **0** and **100** degrees Celsius. Save the query as **Melt**.

14. Create a new table with three fields:

    Atomic Number, **Long Integer Number** field

    Year Discovered, **Long Integer Number** field

    Discovered by, **40** character **Text** field

15. Save the table as **History** and make **Atomic Number** the primary key. Add the following three records to the **History** table:

Atomic Number	Year Discovered	Discovered by
7	1772	Rutherford
12	1755	Davy
32	1886	Winkler

16. Create a relationship between the **Elements** table and the **History** table based on the **Atomic Number** field. What type of link is created? Enforce referential integrity.

17. Use the wizard to create a columnar form including all the fields from the **Elements** table. Save the form as **Element Data**.

18. Edit **Element Data** and add a title of **Element Data Form** to the **Form Header** area. Include your name at the left edge of the **Form Footer** and save the form.

19. Use the **Element Data** form to find the record for **Sulphur**. Ensure the paper size is **A4** and print a copy of the form for the **Sulphur** record only.

20. Use the wizard to create a landscape stepped report showing all the fields from the **Elements** table, grouped by **Classification**. Ensure all data is fully displayed and save the report as **List**. Close the **Chemistry** database.

Exercise 5.18

1. Which of the following is not a common use of a large scale database?

    a) maintenance of hospital patient details

    b) calculation of office accounts

    c) maintenance of government records

    d) airline booking systems.

2. Open the database **Hire**. Some items on the database are obsolete. Delete the table **Cars**, the form **Car Details** and the report **Stock**.

3. Open the **Vehicles** table in datasheet view, showing details of some of the available vehicles owned by a small car hire company. Make sure all data and headings are displayed in full.

4. Add a validation rule to the **Type** field so that it will only accept entries of **Compact**, **Family** or **Sports**. Set the **Validation Text** to list the allowed values in the event of an invalid entry being made.

5. Add a new field to the end of the **Vehicles** table called **Charge**. The data type is to be **Currency** with **0** decimal places. Apply a validation rule to the **Charge** field so that no charge greater than **150** is allowed.

6. Add **Charge** data to all existing records according to the following table:

Type	Charge
Compact	50
Family	75
Sports	90

7. Create a new table called **Bookings** with no primary key, to hold details of vehicle bookings as follows:

Field Name	Data Type	Format
Name	Text	30 characters
Vehicle Number	Number	Long Integer
Start Date	Date	Short Date
Number of Days	Number	Integer
Deposit Paid	Yes/No	Default value **Yes**

8. Create a relationship between the new **Bookings** table and the **Vehicles** table based on the only field that is common to both tables. Apply referential integrity to the relationship.

9. Use the wizard to create a columnar form including all the fields from the **Bookings** table. Save the form as **Booking Form**.

10. Edit the **Booking Form** so that a title of **Booking Entry** appears in the **Form Header** area. Save the form and use it to enter the following bookings for vehicles 211, 212, 214 and 314.

Name	Vehicle Number	Start Date	Number of Days	Deposit Paid
G. Khan	211	29/05/10	3	Yes
A. Smith	212	29/05/10	4	No
D. McKenna	214	02/06/10	5	No
J. Kirk	314	03/06/10	7	Yes

11. The vehicle number **314** is incorrect, it should be **313**. Search for number **314** and replace it with **313**.

12. Create and run a query which lists all **Compact** vehicles from the **Vehicles** table. Show all fields from the table. Save the query as **Compact**. Print a copy of the result of the **Compact** query.

13. Create a query with fields **Vehicle Number**, **Start Date** and **Number of Days** from the **Bookings** table, together with **Type** and **Charge** from the **Vehicles** table. Save the query as **Enquiry**. Print a copy of the **Enquiry** query in **Landscape** orientation.

14. Delete the **Compact** query.

15. Create a **Landscape** orientation report based on all the fields from the **Vehicles** table grouped by **Type** of vehicle and sorted by **Vehicle Number**. Save the report as **Types** and print a copy. Edit the **Types** report. Change the report header to **Vehicle Listing** and remove the **Seats** field (and its heading) from the report.

16. Create a **Landscape** orientation report based on all the fields from the **Enquiry** query. Using the default grouping options, group the report by **Start Date**. Show the sum of **Number of Days** as a summary total. Save the report as **Booking List**.

17. Edit the report so that in the **Page Footer** area, the date appears on the left and your name appears on the right. Remove any other content from the area.

18. Create a calculated field at the right of each report detail line which multiplies the **Number of Days** by **Charge**. Format the field as **Currency**.

19. Save the report and print a copy then close the **Hire** database.

Exercise 5.19

1. A database consists of a single table, which contains data relating to customers, products and orders. How could it be improved?

2. The table contains a single field for each order line, e.g. 7 Widgets, £25 each . Why is this not good practice?

3. Open the database **Wages** and open the **Staff** table. In what sequence are the **Staff** records shown by default?

4. Which navigation button would select the last record in the table? Does the same button apply in queries and forms?

5. Use help to find out the function of indexes. Create an index called **Name** based on the **Surname** field. Define ascending order with duplicates not allowed (note this will not automatically reorder the data). Do not replace the **Primary Key** index.

6. Filter the table to show only employees in the **Production** department.

7. Sort the filtered table in ascending order of **Age**.

8. Print a copy of the sorted filtered table then remove all filters/sorts.

9. Filter the table to show only employees who are not in the **Production** department.

10. Sort the filtered table in descending order of **Rate**.

11. Print a copy of the sorted filtered table then remove all filters/sorts.

12. Create a query showing all fields from the **Staff** table, for all employees who have started the company since **1st January 2000**. Save the query as **New Starters** and print a copy of the results.

13. Create a query to see if there are any employees in the **Testing** department who are over **50** years old. Show all fields from the **Staff** table in the resulting list. Save the query as **Old Testers** and print a copy of the results.

14. Create the following table to hold details of the hours worked by each employee.

Field Name	Data Type	Format
Staff No	Number	Long Integer
Date	Date	Short Date
Hours Worked	Number	Integer

15. Save the table as **Hours** with no primary key.

16. Create a relationship between the **Hours** table and the **Staff** table based on an appropriate field from each table.

17. Create a landscape report, based on the **Staff** table, which is grouped by **Department**, and sorted on **Staff No**. Save the report as **Staff List**.

18. The **Staff List** report will need to be edited so that the title **Department Listing** is shown in the report header.

Department Listing

Department	Staff No	Surname	First Name	Start Date	Age	Rate
Despatch						
	3	Patel	Nora	05.05.1995	48	£18.60
	15	Dumalu	Mara	21.09.1995	53	£19.60
	17	Peters	Shaun	31.12.1999	32	£18.60
Finishing						
	6	Kumar	Ravi	27.11.2003	18	£19.60
	9	Singh	Gita	13.01.2000	36	£19.60
	11	Hussan	Tariq	27.09.1995	47	£19.60
	16	Neville	David	13.07.1999	29	£17.50
Maintenance						
	1	Thompson	James	30.12.2002	30	£22.00
	7	Ripley	Ellen	12.06.1998	35	£24.00
	12	Smith	David	18.02.1990	52	£22.40
Production						
	2	Ingam	Ian	24.02.1990	53	£23.20
	4	Tresori	Gina	10.04.2002	37	£20.40
	5	Branson	Paul	01.03.1997	36	£20.40
	8	Jones	Timothy	17.10.2001	43	£20.40
	13	Yomani	Asif	08.05.1999	40	£24.00
	14	Brown	John	08.05.1994	40	£22.40

16 August 2005

Page 1 of 2

19. Paul Branson has left the company. Locate his record in the table and delete it. Add your own details with Paul Branson's old **Staff No**. Assign yourself to the **Production** department with an hourly rate of **20**.

20. Print a copy of the **Staff List** report with your name included and then close the **Wages** database.

Exercise 5.20

1. Who would be responsible for the recovery of a database after a crash?

    a) a database user

    b) a database specialist

    c) a database administrator.

2. Open the database **Production**. This database for a small manufacturing company includes a table of the manufacturing output of their three main products for each month of the year and a table to hold orders for their products.

3. Change the data type of the **Product** field in the **Orders** table to **Text**, with a length of **20** characters.

4. Open the **Relationships** window. The link between the **Orders** table and the **Output2009** table is meaningless. Delete it.

5. Create a new relationship between the **Orders** and the **Products** tables using the **Product** field.

6. Open the **Output2009** table in datasheet view and sort the table by **Month**. Why are the records not in date order? Remove all filters and sorts.

7. Add a new field as the first field in the **Output2009** table. The field name is **Month No**, data type is **Numeric, Integer**.

8. Enter appropriate values in the new field for all records, i.e. 1 for January, 2 for February, 12 for December.

9. Sort the amended table by **Month No**. Filter the table to show only sales quantities for the month of **November**. Print the filtered list then remove all filters and sorts.

10. Create a query based on the **Output2009** table showing only sales of **Widget**, arranged in ascending order of **Quantity**. Show all fields from the table and save the query as **Performance**.

11. Print a single copy of the resulting list.

12. The highest output quantities seem to be in the last 3 months of the year. To see if there are any exceptions, amend the **Performance** query to show records for all products with output greater than **4000** for months before **October**, i.e. month numbers less than **10**. Which records are found? Save the amended query as **Exceptions**.

13. Create a report showing all fields from the **Output2009** table, grouped by **Month No**, sorted by **Product**, showing **Sum** summary values for **Quantity**. The report is to be in **Portrait** orientation and have a title of **Output by Month**.

14. Amend the report by changing the font of the report title to **Arial**, extending the size of the label if necessary to ensure that the title is still fully displayed. Include your name so that it appears once at the end of the report.

15. Print a copy of the report. Which month has the highest overall total output? What is the overall output quantity for all products for the year?

16. Create another report, similar to **Output by Month**, but grouped by **Product** and sorted by **Month No**. Both **Sum** and **Average** summary values for quantity are to be displayed and the report is to be given a title of **Output by Product**.

17. Amend the report by changing the font of the title to **Arial**, **Italic**. Change the sum and average summary values (and their labels) to **Arial** and their colour to **Red**. Ensure that all data and text is fully displayed. Save the report.

18. Create a simple form which will allow all fields on the **Orders** table to be entered. Save the form as **Order Entry**. Enter an order from **Global Engines Company** for **100 Widgets** with today's date. Print a copy of this order.

19. Export the table **Output2009** in **text file** format with the same name to the data folder. Export the **Performance** query in **text file** format with the same name, then close any open objects and close the **Production** database.

Exercise 5.21

1. Open the database **Geography** and open the **Mountains** table in datasheet view, showing details of some of the highest mountains in various parts of the world. Make sure that all data and labels are fully displayed.

2. Sort the table in order of date first climbed, with the most recently climbed appearing first in the list. Which was the last of these mountains to be climbed in the nineteenth century?

3. Print a copy of the sorted table.

4. Sort the table in descending order of height and apply a filter so that only mountains higher than **8000** metres are shown. What do they all have in common?

5. Remove all filters and sorts. Create a query which lists all the mountains in the **Alps** range. Show all fields from the table and save the query as **Alps**.

6. Amend the query so that the records are sorted in order of **Height (metres)** and remove the **Height (feet)** field from the output. Save the query.

7. Create another query which shows all mountains between 5000 and 7000 metres high. How many are shown? Save the query as **Medium**.

8. Create a third query displaying all fields to show all mountains in Africa or Asia and save as **Africa Asia**. Remove the criteria and edit the query by using the wildcard **A*A**. Save the changes to the query.

9. Use the wizard to create a columnar form showing all the fields query. Save the form as **Alpine**.

10. How many records can be viewed using this form?

11. Use the form to find and display the record for the **Matterhorn**. Obtain a print out of the form for this record only. Delete this record using the form.

12. Create the following table to hold details of some of the world's longest rivers.

Field Name	Data Type	Format
Name	Text	Length 50
Continent	Text	Length 50
Starts	Text	Length 50
Ends	Text	Length 50
Length (km)	Number	Long Integer

13. Define **Name** as the primary key and save the table as **Rivers**.

14. Add a record for the river **Nile** in **Africa**, which starts in **Lake Victoria**, ends in the **Mediterranean Sea**, and is **6690km** long. Where necessary, resize column widths so that all data is fully displayed.

15. Change the format of the **Length** field to **Integer**. Save the table.

16. Create a report showing all fields from the **Mountains** table except **Height(feet)** and **First Ascent**, grouped by **Continent**, sorted by **Name**, showing the maximum and minimum mountain height in metres for each continent. The report is to be in **Portrait** orientation and have a title of **Continents**.

17. Amend the **Continents** report in **Design View** so that it looks similar to the following example. The report title is **24pt** and **red**. The continent names are **14pt bold** and **italic**. A text label has been removed from the **Continent** footer and some fields and labels have been moved, resized or amended.

Continent	Name	Country	Range	Height (m)	First Ascent
Africa					
	Kenya	Kenya	Volcano	5199	1899
	Kilimanjaro	Tanzania	Volcano	5895	1889
	Toubkal	Morocco	Atlas	4165	1923
			Min	4165	
			Max	5895	

Peaks of the World

18. Include your name so that it appears once at the bottom of every page, in the centre of the page. Print a copy of the report.

19. Delete the **Test** query from the database, then close the **Geography** database and close *Access*.

The following revision exercises are divided into sections, each targeted at specific elements of the ECDL module *Presentation Software*. The individual sections are an exact match for the sections in the ECDL training guides from CiA Training, making the guides an ideal reference source for anyone working through these exercises.

31. Getting Started

These exercises include topics taken from the following list: understanding *PowerPoint* principles, starting *PowerPoint*, using **wizards** or **templates**, recognising the screen layout, using help, changing preferences and exiting *PowerPoint*.

Exercise 6.1

1. Start *PowerPoint* and start a new blank presentation.

2. Set the **Author** to **William Shakespeare**.

3. What single key press will start the *PowerPoint* **Help** function?

4. On which **Menu** or **Ribbon Tab** would you find the **Rehearse Timings** button?

5. Where would you be able to see the **Outline** view of your presentation?

6. Use **ToolTips** to discover name of the following buttons:

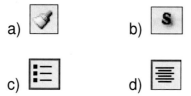

7. Use the **Help function** to find some general information about the **slide master**.

8. Close **Help**.

9. Give 3 features of slide content which would contribute to good practice.

10. Close *PowerPoint*.

Exercise 6.2

1. Open *PowerPoint*.

2. Use the **AutoContent Wizard** (*XP/2003*) or one of the installed sample templates (*2007/2010/2013*) to create a new presentation.

3. Change the **Title** to **Revision Presentation** and change the subtitle to your name.

4. Depending on the version of *PowerPoint*, either hide the **Standard** and **Formatting** toolbars or minimise the **Ribbon**.

5. Redisplay the features hidden in the previous step.

6. Assuming an image is selected, what does the ▨ button do, on the **Picture** toolbar or **Picture Tools** ribbon tab?

7. Check the current default file location for saves then change it to **CIA DATA FILES**.

8. Check the current time period for saving **AutoRecover** information then change it to **15** minutes.

9. Change the previous two settings back to their original values.

10. Close *PowerPoint*, clicking **No** if prompted to save.

32. Slides & Presentations

These exercises include topics taken from the following list: understanding and using different views, understanding slide show basics, saving, closing and opening presentations, using presentation/design templates, creating a blank presentation, adding new slides, inserting slides and changing slide layout and background.

Exercise 6.3

1. Open the **Computers** presentation.

2. Switch to **Outline View**.

3. On slide 4 **Printer and Scanner** enter the final bullet point **Sometimes printer and scanner are all in one**.

4. **Collapse All** slides so only the titles can be seen.

5. Move the **Printer and Scanner** slide above the **Mouse, Keyboard and Speakers** slide.

6. Switch to **Slide Sorter View**.

7. Move the **Printer and Scanner** slide back to the end of the presentation.

8. Switch to **Notes Page View** and read the notes on each of the pages.

9. Add a **light blue** background to the **Title Slide** of the presentation.

10. Insert 4 new slides at the end of the presentation: a title slide, a chart and text slide, a bulleted list slide and a table slide. Add titles to each slide that describe their layout.

11. Add the following text as a presenter note to the table slide:
    Make sure the latest table is available.

12. Save the presentation in rich text format as **Computers2**.

13. Delete the four new slides just added.

14. Save the presentation as a show named **Computers Show**.

15. Open the presentation **Lodgings** and save in the data file location as a template named **Kennel Template**.

16. Switch back to the **Computers Show** presentation.

17. Save the presentation as a normal presentation **Computers3** and close it.

18. Close the **Kennel** template.

Exercise 6.4

1. Create a new blank presentation. By default, what is the layout of the first slide?

2. On the first slide, add the title text **Solar System**.

3. Click to add the **Subtitle 'by Your Name'**.

4. Insert a **New Slide** using a layout with a **Title** and a single block of content (text).

5. Click to add the title **The Sun**.

6. Why is it a good idea to give different, meaningful titles to the slides in a presentation?

7. Add 9 new slides with the same layout, with the following titles:

   - **Mercury**
   - **Venus**
   - **Earth**
   - **Mars**
   - **Jupiter**
   - **Saturn**
   - **Uranus**
   - **Neptune**
   - **Pluto**

8. Apply a dark colour scheme to all slides.

9. Save slide **1** as an image file in **.png** format, called **Solar System.png**.

10. Add a presenter note to slide **5 Earth**: **The only planet known to support life**.

11. View the presentation in **Slide Show View**.

12. Save the presentation as **Planets**.

13. Close the presentation.

33. Formatting

These exercises include topics taken from the following list: applying formatting, text effects and bullets, using undo and redo, changing alignment and spacing, using cut, copy and paste, using animation schemes and custom animation, applying headers & footers, working with master pages and checking spelling.

Exercise 6.5

1. Open the **Computers** presentation.

2. In Normal view, note the current value for the **Zoom** percentage then view the first slide at a **Zoom** of **100%**.

3. Change the **Zoom** percentage to **25%** then return it to its original value.

4. Add a **White Marble Texture Background** to the **Slide Master** and a **light blue** background to the **Title Master**.

5. Change the fonts on the **Slide Master** and **Title Master** to **Verdana** and the size of the title text to **40pt**. Left align all titles.

6. Change the colour of the text on the masters to red so the text stands out clearly.

7. On the **Title Master** only, add a footer containing your name. Change the case of the footer text to upper case.

8. Switch to **Normal** view and on the **2**nd slide add **Custom Animation** to the 2 pictures so they run as soon as the slide is opened.

9. Delete the bullet points on slide **3**.

10. Use the **Undo** button to bring back the bullet points.

11. Add **Custom Animation** to the images on the other slides.

12. Remove all animations from slide **2**.

13. Add a **Date** to the presentation which **Automatically Updates** and the **Slide Number** to each slide.

14. Copy slide 2 and paste it at the end of the presentation.

15. Now <u>move</u> the last slide and paste it into a new, blank presentation.

16. Copy the bulleted text from slide **3** and paste it into a new title and text slide in the new presentation. Add the title **Input Devices**.

17. In the **Computers** presentation copy the first bullet point from slide **2** and paste it as the last bullet point on slide **4**.

18. Delete the last bullet point on slide **4**.

19. Reduce the font size of the body text where necessary to ensure it fits each slide.

20. Save the presentation as **Computer Formatted** and close it. Close the other presentation <u>without</u> saving.

Exercise 6.6

1. Open the **Power Shower** presentation.

2. Apply the **Textured Design Template** (*XP/2003*) or the **Verve** theme (*2007/2010/2013*) to the presentation.

3. Copy **Slide 2** and paste it as a new slide **3**.

4. Add the **Oak Texture** to the background of the new slide **3** and change the text colour on this slide to yellow.

5. Draw a rectangle which covers all of the text. Change the background colour of the rectangle to **white**.

6. Send the rectangle to the back so that the content can be seen.

7. Change the text colour on this slide to a darker colour.

8. On this slide, **Customize** the **Bullets** to be a **Pen Symbol**.

9. Change the font, colour and size of the title to make it stand out.

10. Change the **Line Spacing** of this slide to be **1.5** and increase the indent of the bullets. Increase the size of the white box if necessary to include the text.

11. Decrease the indent to its original setting and centre the bulleted text.

12. Add your name, a non-updating date and a slide number in the **Footer** area of each slide except slide **1**.

13. Check the spelling on the whole presentation. Save the presentation as **Shower Formatted** and close it.

34. *PowerPoint Objects*

These exercises include topics taken from the following list: inserting and modifying an organisation chart, moving, resizing and copying objects, inserting and animating **Clip Art**, inserting a picture/chart, using drawing tools and **AutoShapes** on slides, selecting, rotating and flipping objects, arranging and distributing objects, changing object colours and importing images.

Exercise 6.7

1. Open a new blank presentation.

2. Insert an animated **Clip Art**, into the top right of the **Slide Master**. Try searching for **ball** (*XP/2003*) or **walk** (*2007/2010/2013*).

3. Increase the size of the image.

4. Add an automatically updating date to the bottom of the **Slide Master**.

5. Apply an entrance animation to the title and a different one to the image.

6. Add 2 more **Clip Art** images (non-animated) to the bottom left of the slide.

7. Reduce the size of the images and flip the second one.

8. Overlap the images and bring the bottom image forward. Delete the top image.

9. Change the colour of the **Title** to **dark red**.

10. Add a **dark red** rectangle around the image at the bottom left of the slide. Change the line colour to darkest red and the weight of the line to **1½pt**.

11. Change the background colour of the rectangle to a lighter red and send this rectangle to the back.

12. Close master view and add the slide title **Images** and your name as the subtitle.

13. Add a new blank slide and draw the following shapes: a line, a block arrow, a line arrow, a square, an oval, a circle.

14. Add your name to each shape apart from the line and the arrow and change their colour to dark red.

15. Change the style of both ends of the line arrow and increase its weight to **3pt**.

16. Run the slide show to see the animation effects.

17. Save the presentation as **Images** and close it.

Exercise 6.8

1. Open the **Power Shower** presentation.

2. Move to slide 3, delete the grey text and alter the slide layout to include an organisation chart.

3. Add a chart with the following staff positions:

    Manager with **Assistant Manager**, **Product Manager**, **Sales Manager** and **Customer Services Manager** all as subordinates of the manager.

4. Add an additional assistant manager and remove the customer services manager.

5. Apply a different style to the **Organization Chart**.

6. Insert a new, **Title Only** slide at the end of the presentation and add the title **Office Layout**.

7. Draw a large rectangle below the title to represent the office floor.

8. Search **Clip Art** for **office layout** to display a selection of room layout shapes.

9. Create an office layout according to the following instructions; moving, rotating and resizing of objects will be required. A picture of the final layout is included in the answer section.

10. Place a large, rectangular **Desk** in the centre of the room. Place 8 **Desk Chairs** around the desk with half of each chair hidden under the desk.

11. Add a **Door Swing** to the bottom left and top right of the room, aligning them relative to the slide.

12. Add 2 **File Cabinets** to the left wall and a **Floor Lamp** to the bottom right corner. Delete a file cabinet from the left wall.

13. Add a long narrow **Desk** to the top wall. Place a **Telephone** on the long desk. Group all objects on the slide.

14. Insert a **Water Clip Art** picture on the first slide.

15. Save the presentation as **Shower2**.

16. Copy the organisation chart to a new, blank presentation with a title only slide.

17. Copy the telephone from the office layout slide in the **Shower2** presentation (you will need to ungroup the shapes) and paste it at the top right corner of the title only slide in the new presentation.

18. Paste the telephone again on to the long desk in the original **Shower2** presentation, so there are now 2 telephones. Regroup the shapes.

19. Save and close the **Shower2** presentation. Close the other presentation without saving.

Exercise 6.9

1. Start a new, blank presentation and save it as **Figures**.

2. Change the layout of the slide so that a table can be added and add the title **Cruise Bookings**.

3. Create a table and enter the following data:

Cruise Bookings			
	2007	2008	2009
Eastern Star	2500	2450	2700
Southern Star	3100	3280	3400

4. Select the top row and fill with a turquoise/aqua background colour.

5. Select the left column and fill with the same colour.

6. Select the whole table and change the font to **Verdana 20pt**.

7. Insert rows beneath the existing rows to contain the following data: **Northern Star**, 2007 - **1750**, 2008 - **1900** and 2009 - **2500**; **Western Star**, 2007 - **1900**, 2008 - **2500**, 2009 - **3100**. Adjust the height of the rows appropriately.

8. Insert a new column for 2010.

9. You have been informed that details for 2010 are unavailable. Delete the column and adjust column widths as appropriate.

10. Insert a new **Title Only** slide with the title **Chart**.

11. Open the presentation **Bright Line**. Copy the chart from slide **2** on to the new **Chart** slide in the **Figures** presentation.

12. Change the chart to a line chart. This is an unsuitable chart type for this data. Change it to a bar chart.

13. Add a chart title of **Cruise Bookings**. Display data labels on the chart, showing values in the **Outside End** position. Format all data labels as **Arial**, **11pt**.

14. Edit the chart title to **Bookings**.

15. Change the background colour of the chart to pale green and change the colour of the bars for some of the series.

16. Decrease the size of the chart slightly. Make sure the labels are still clear enough to read and the chart title is not overlapping the chart.

17. Save the **Figures** presentation.

18. Print the **Chart** slide only. The **Cruise Bookings** chart is not needed - delete it.

19. Close the **Figures** presentation <u>without</u> saving and close the **Bright Line** presentation <u>without</u> saving.

35. *Slide Shows*

These exercises include topics taken from the following list: selecting the correct output format, setting up a slide show, applying slide transitions and timings, running the presentation and printing slides, presentations and handouts.

Exercise 6.10

1. Open the **Computers** presentation.

2. Add a suitable **Design Template** or **Design Theme** to all of the presentation.

3. Add **Random** slide transitions to the slides.

4. View the slide show from the first slide.

5. Hide the **Mouse, Keyboard and Speakers** slide.

6. Use **Undo** so that the slide will be included again.

7. Use **Redo** so that the slide will be hidden.

8. Remove the slide transitions.

9. View the slide show again from the current slide and during the show, right click and select the hidden slide.

10. Reapply the slide transitions.

11. Print all **4** slides as **Handouts**, 2 slides to a page.

12. Print slides **2** and **3**, including their **Notes** pages.

13. Save the presentation as **Computers4**.

14. Set up the page settings for viewing on an overhead projector.

15. Save the presentation as **Computers5**.

16. Print <u>2</u> copies of slide **4** only.

17. Close the presentation.

Exercise 6.11

1. Open the **Tropical Fish** presentation.

2. Change the **Orientation** of the **Slides** to **Portrait**.

3. Apply the **Ocean Design** template (*XP/2003*) or the **Flow** theme (*2007/2010/2013*) to all of the slides.

4. Apply timings to the slide show.

5. Set up the slide show as an on screen show, to **Loop Continuously** and ensure the **Timings** are used.

6. View the slide show to check the timings

7. Apply a different slide transition to each of the pages.

8. View the slide show to view the transitions.

9. While viewing the show, when you get to slide **3**, navigate back to the first slide. Now go to the next slide and carry on viewing the show.

10. Ensure the paper size is **A4** and print the slides as handouts with 3 on a sheet.

11. Print an outline of the slides.

12. Save the presentation as **Ocean Fish**.

13. Close the presentation.

The following revision exercises can involve processes from any part of the ECDL module *Presentation Software.*

Exercise 6.12

1. Open the **Computers** presentation. Set the **Author** field to your name.

2. Move the **Mouse, Keyboard and Speakers** slide to be the final slide of the presentation.

3. Add the following text as a further presenter note to this slide:
   A wireless keyboard and mouse can be used.

4. Add a new slide at the end of the presentation and insert a column chart. Add a title of **Chart 1** and edit the chart data to match the following:

	Tower	Monitor	Printer	Scanner	Speakers	Keyboard	Mouse
% of Total Price	52	16	12	10	4	3	3

5. If you are using *PowerPoint 2007, 2010 or 2013*, select **Switch Row/Column** after adding the data.

6. Change the chart to be a **Pie Chart**. Change the colour of each of the slices of pie and change the chart background to a coordinating colour. Add data labels to show values.

7. Copy the chart to a new slide, inserted at the end of the presentation. Change the chart to a line chart and change the title to **Chart 2**.

8. On the **Slide Master**, change the colour of the **Title Text** to be **blue** and make it italic.

9. Undo the italic formatting. Change the fonts on the **Slide Master** to **Tahoma** and change the line spacing before and after the bullets to **6pt**.

10. Add a background picture, **Leads.jpg** to the **Slide Master**.

11. Insert the **Keyboard.gif** picture at the top left of the **Slide Master**.

12. Send the picture to the **Back**.

13. Add a **light blue** background to the **Title Master**.

14. Use **Slide Master** to add the same animation entrance effect to the title and content of all slides. Set the trigger for each effect to be **Start with Previous**.

15. Apply a **Date** to all slides which updates automatically.

16. Add a slide transition effect with an automatic 3 second timing to all slides.

17. Set up the slide show to **Loop Continuously**

18. Print slides 2, 3 and 4 on a single sheet with space to write your own notes.

19. Save the presentation as **Computer Parts** and close it.

Exercise 6.13

1. Open the **Football News** presentation.

2. Add the design template or theme, **Football** from the data files.

3. Insert slide numbers and an automatically updating date to the footer of all slides.

4. Change all of the text to **White** and increase the indent of bullets on the slide master.

5. Add a new slide to the end of the presentation and insert a column chart.

6. Add a title, **Match Performances** to the slide and underline it.

7. Edit the chart content to match the following:

	Game 1	Game 2	Game 3	Game 4
Player A	8	6	6	7
Player B	10	9	9	10
Player C	9	10	7	2

8. If you are using *PowerPoint 2007, 2010 or 2013*, select **Switch Row/Column** after adding the data.

9. Change the text associated with the chart to **White**.

10. On the **Slide Master** change the **Line Spacing** to **1.5**.

11. Add a **Soccer** Clip Art image to the top right of every page.

12. Resize the image the image to about 4cm wide and send the image backwards until it appears behind any text.

13. Add **Transitions** with a slow speed to the slides in the presentation.

14. Print all of the slides as a handout on a single page.

15. View the slide show.

16. Save the presentation as **Football**.

17. Save the presentation as a *PowerPoint* show, **Football Show** and close it.

Exercise 6.14

1. Open the template **New Invention** from the supplied data folder.

2. Apply the **Echo Design** template (*XP/2003*) or the **Origin** theme (*2007/2010/2013*).

3. Format the background of all slides with a preset gradient fill of **Daybreak**.

4. Display **Outline View**.

5. Move the **Our Strengths** slide above the **Cost Analysis** slide.

6. Delete the **Next Steps** slide.

7. On the **Title Master**, insert the **Dots.gif** picture and move it to the top right corner.

8. Use the **Set Transparent Color** button, , to remove the **white** from the picture. This is found on the **Pictures** toolbar in *XP/2003* and in the **Recolor** or **Color** function on the **Picture Tools Format** tab in *2007/2010/2013*.

9. On the **Slide Master**, insert the **Dots.gif** picture, resize it to about half size, move it to the bottom left corner (inside the margins) and again make the white background transparent.

10. Change the title font on the **Slide Master** to dark red and italic.

11. Insert a slide after the **Our Strengths** slide and add a simple **Organisation Chart**. Enter a slide title of **The Team** and use the picture below as a model but use whatever names you like.

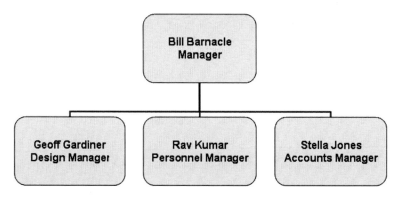

12. The manager needs some help. Add an assistant to Bill Barnacle called **Lisa Lott, PA**.

13. **Omit** or **Hide** all background graphics from this slide only.

14. Change the orientation of the slides to **Portrait**.

15. Add a single slide transition to every slide.

16. View the slide show.

17. Change the orientation back to **Landscape**.

18. Save the presentation in the supplied data folder as a template called **Invention Template** and close it.

Exercise 6.15

1. Open the **Flag Quiz** presentation.

2. Import the image **Ireland Flag.gif** to the space on slide **3**.

3. Insert a text box between the **Greece** and **EU** text and add the text **Ireland**. Right align the text.

4. Change the text colour to **light blue**.

5. Preview slide 3 only. Notice that the new text does not move. Add a **Custom Animation** of a **Custom Line Motion Path** to this text so it moves to the correct position.

6. Preview slide 3 again to check all of the animation.

7. Change the background on the **Slide Master** to a **light blue**. Move back to **Normal** view to see that the text on the flag slides (3-6) is difficult or impossible to see.

8. Draw a long rectangular box around all of the text at the bottom of these 4 slides. Change the fill colour of the box to a **dark blue** and send the box to the **Back**.

9. Apply **Bold** and **Shadow** to the **Title** on the **Master Slide**.

10. Change the bullet style to a **Picture Bullet** of your choice.

11. Display **Slide Sorter** view and move the **European Flags** slide after the **Easy European Flags** slide.

12. Change the text colour on slides **2** and **7** to **black** to ensure it can be read clearly.

13. Insert a suitable picture of a **Globe** into the top right corner of each slide.

14. Move the **Difficult European Flags** to the end of the presentation.

15. Set up the slide show to stop at the 6th slide.

16. Apply **Random Slide Transitions** to the whole presentation and view the whole slide show.

17. Change the paper size to **Letter**. Print slide 2 to confirm the rules.

18. Save the presentation as **Flag Quiz Complete**.

19. Now save the presentation in rich text format as **Flags Brief** and close it.

Exercise 6.16

1. Create a new, blank presentation.

2. Add the title, **Sport** to the slide and centre align it.

3. Insert slides with the following left aligned titles: **Cricket**, **Tennis**, **Basketball**, **Badminton**, and space for a single column of text.

4. Add a **Clip Art** image to the top right of each of the slides, searching for the appropriate sport name for that slide.

5. Insert a new slide after **Basketball**, titled **Rugby** and add a suitable **Clip Art** image.

6. Add a **Two Color** (2 **greens**) **Diagonal Gradient Fill Effect** to all of the slides.

7. Change all of the fonts on the **Slide Master** to **Impact** and increase the size slightly.

8. Change the colour of the title to a **dark blue** and the other text to **yellow**.

9. Add your name to the **Footer**. Change your name to upper case.

10. Add a **Smiley Face** shape to the bottom left of the **Master Slide** and change the **Fill Colour** of this shape to the **Moss Gradient Effect**.

11. Copy this shape.

12. Close **Master View** and on the first slide only, **Paste** the shape, as many times as required to fill the bottom of the slide, ensuring they are aligned relative to the slide.

13. Alter the **Fill Effects** of these shapes to different **Preset Gradients**.

14. Add **Random Slide Transitions** to the presentation.

15. Set up the show to be viewed on an overhead projector.

16. View the slide show.

17. Save all the slides in **.gif** image format, named **sports clips**.

18. Save the presentation as **Sport**.

19. Close the presentation.

Exercise 6.17

1. Create a new, blank presentation and save it as **Kennels**. Check in options that your name is shown as the user name and that the default saving location for files is **My Documents** or **Documents**.

2. You are going to create part of this presentation using information from an existing file. Open the presentation **Lodgings**. Spell check this presentation and correct any errors found.

3. Copy the text from the first slide of this presentation to the first slide in the **Kennels** presentation. Copy the graphics on the **Lodgings** master slide and paste them into the master slide in the **Kennels** presentation.

4. Copy the **Features** slide from **Lodgings** and paste it at the end of the **Kennels** presentation. Create a new slide with a layout that will include a title and two areas for content to contain a chart and some text.

5. Copy the chart from the **Customer Satisfaction** slide in **Lodgings** to the new slide.

6. Move the associated text from the slide in **Lodgings** and paste it at the right of the chart in **Kennels**. Add the title **Bookings**.

7. Close **Lodgings** without saving.

8. On the slide master, change the title text to **Comic Sans MS 40pt**, the text styles to the same font, **28pt** and the second level text to the same font, **20pt**.

9. Apply a preset gradient effect of **Calm Water** to the slide background.

10. Delete the graphic at the left of the slide. Rotate the remaining graphic clockwise slightly, until the kennel is level. Ensure it is aligned relative to the slide in the top right corner.

11. On slide **2 Features**, flip the central graphic horizontally.

12. Change the chart on the **Bookings** slide to a line chart and change the line colour to yellow.

13. At the end of the presentation, insert a new slide with a title and space for a table.

14. Add the title **Tariffs**. Insert a table of 2 columns and 4 rows and enter the following information.

Animal	High Season (per day)
Dog	10.00
Cat	8.50
Small animal*	5.00

15. Add a new row to contain a price of **4.50** for **Caged birds**.

16. Add a new column to show the low season daily tariffs as follows: **dogs 8.50**, **cats 6.00**, **small animals** and **caged birds 3.50**.

17. Adjust column widths and row height as appropriate to display the information fully.

18. The manager has developed an allergy to caged birds. Delete the row containing the associated information and adjust the table again if necessary.

19. Draw a small text box below the table and add the following text: *** hamsters, rats, guinea pigs, etc. If you have an animal that is not listed here, please contact us; we may be able to accommodate your pet.**

20. Insert a new **Title Only** slide, with the title **Why choose us?**

21. Draw shapes as in the diagram below and add the text shown to the appropriate shapes.

22. Add shadows to all shapes apart from the thinner arrow, which is **4½pt**.

23. Change the background colour of all shapes to dark turquoise and change the end style of the drawn arrow on the top row to **oval arrow**.

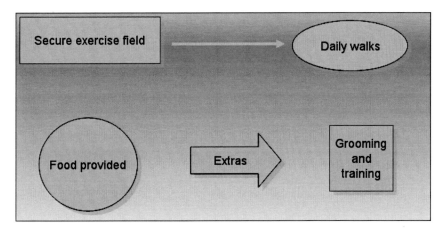

24. Group the shapes and reduce their size very slightly. Ungroup the shapes and change the colour of the **Extras** shape to bright pink. Regroup the shapes.

25. Add a final slide to contain a title and a block of text. Add the title **Contact Us...** and add the following bullet points to the content area:

    By phone on 0121 3456789

    By e-mail at info@barnacles.co.uk

    Or call in to Barnacle Farm, St Swithin's Way, Noplace

26. For this slide only, change the line spacing to **1.5 lines** and the spacing before and after paragraphs to **0.3 lines** or **12pt**. Hide this slide

27. On the slide master, apply a **Fly In** animation effect to the **Title** and **Content** areas so that the effect is seen on all slides.

28. Set the show up to be viewed as an on-screen show. View the show from slide **1**.

29. End the show and then view it from slide **3**. Navigate to the hidden slide during the show. Continue to the end.

30. Print the **Tariffs** slide in **Portrait** orientation then print handouts, 3 to a page.

31. Change the slide orientation back to **Landscape**, save all changes to the presentation and close it.

32. Close *PowerPoint*.

Answers

This section contains answers to all specific questions posed in the preceding exercises, together with the name of the file or files containing the worked solution for each exercise.

Word Processing Software

Exercise 3.1

Step 5   File | Page Setup or the Page Layout tab

Step 6   **Drawing** toolbar or the **Insert** tab

Step 7   Click on a **WordArt** object on the page

Step 8   Tooltips

Exercise 3.2

Step 3   **Standard** toolbar or **Home** tab

Step 4   **Tools** menu or **Page layout** tab

Step 5   <u>No</u>, Dialog boxes cannot be resized and <u>no</u>, they do not appear on the **Taskbar**

Step 6   **Font Colour**

Exercise 3.3

Step 3   The message will ask - **Do you want to save the changes to this document**. The exact wording will vary with the application version

Step 5   **.doc** or **.docx**

Step 7   **Print Layout** view

Step 9   **.rtf**

Step 11   **.dot** or.**dotx**

Sample solutions for this exercise are saved as **Personal Solution, Personal Info Solution** and **Rich Solution** in the **Module 3 Solutions** folder.

Exercise 3.4

Step 4   **.wps**

Step 7   **.txt**

Step 8   Because any formatting in the original document may be lost

Sample solutions for this exercise are saved as **Hobbies Solution, Ballet2 Solution** (*XP/2003* only), **Very Plain Solution** and **My Letter Solution** in the **Module 3 Solutions** folder.

Exercise 3.5

Step 4   b

Step 7   <Ctrl> + click

Step 9   The deleted sentence reappears

A sample solution for this exercise is saved as **Gardens2 Solution** in the **Module 3 Solutions** folder.

Exercise 3.6

Step 9   The required keys are **<Ctrl> + A**

Step 10   All text is deleted and replaced with the letter q

Step 13   The mark **.** indicates a space

A sample solution for this exercise is saved as **Ballet2 Solution** in the **Module 3 Solutions** folder.

Exercise 3.8

Step 7   The font size of the text has been reduced.

Exercise 3.9

A sample solution for this exercise is saved as **Lakes2 Solution** in the **Module 3 Solutions** folder.

Exercise 3.10

A sample solution for this exercise is saved as **Banks2 Solution** in the **Module 3 Solutions** folder.

Exercise 3.11

A sample solution for this exercise is saved as **Tours2 Solution** in the **Module 3 Solutions** folder.

Exercise 3.12

Step 2   Text may be too small to read

Step 3   Cannot see much of the page

Step 5   Toffington, Tarquin and Twiste

Step 6   The phrase is on page 2

Step 7   The word is in the section **The Gardens**

Step 8   4 replacements are made

Exercise 3.13

Step 2   a) It's best to use the align, indent or tab tools

A sample solution for this exercise is saved as **Lakes3 Solution** in the **Module 3 Solutions** folder.

Exercise 3.14

Step 1   It's best to use the paragraph spacing settings

Sample solutions for this exercise are saved as **List2 Solution** and **Overtime List 2 Solution** in the **Module 3 Solutions** folder.

Exercise 3.15

Step 2   The **Windows** menu in *XP/2003*; the **View** tab and **Switch Windows** button in *2007/2010/2013*

A sample solution for this exercise is saved as **Gardens3 Solution** in the **Module 3 Solutions** folder.

Exercise 3.16

Step 8   Only in **Print Layout** view

A sample solution for this exercise is saved as **Rocks2 Solution** in the **Module 3 Solutions** folder.

Exercise 3.17

A sample solution for this exercise is saved as **Mountains Solution** in the **Module 3 Solutions** folder.

Exercise 3.18

A sample solution for this exercise is saved as **Log Solution** in the **Module 3 Solutions** folder.

Exercise 3.19

A sample solution for this exercise is saved as **Lakes4 Solution** in the **Module 3 Solutions** folder.

Exercise 3.20

Step 1   It's better to use a page break to create a new page

Step 11   Only 1 page break per page

Step 12   Portrait and Landscape

A sample solution for this exercise is saved as **Hall2 Solution** in the **Module 3 Solutions** folder.

Exercise 3.21

Sample solutions for this exercise are saved as **Offer Solution** and **Letters3 Solution** in the **Module 3 Solutions** folder.

Exercise 3.22

A sample solution for this exercise is saved as **Letters4 Solution** in the **Module 3 Solutions** folder.

Exercise 3.23

Step 10   Any corner handle

A sample solution for this exercise is saved as **Ballet3 Solution** in the **Module 3 Solutions** folder.

Exercise 3.24

A sample solution for this exercise is saved as **Outdoor Solution** in the **Module 3 Solutions** folder.

Exercise 3.25

Step 1   d) **Status Bar**

Sample solutions for this exercise are saved as **Rhyme Solution**, **Apply2 Solution** and **Applications Solution** in the **Module 3 Solutions** folder.

Exercise 3.26

Sample solutions for this exercise are saved as **My Memo Solution** and **Holiday Plan2 Solution** in the **Module 3 Solutions** folder.

Exercise 3.27

Sample solutions for this exercise are saved as **Thanks Solution**, **Thanksmerge Solution** and **Report2 Solution** in the **Module 3 Solutions** folder.

Exercise 3.28

Step 5   There are two occurrences of the word **Biology**

Step 18   All formatting including the chart is lost if a document is saved in a **.txt** format

Sample solutions for this exercise are saved as **Science2 Solution** and **Science Text Solution** in the **Module 3 Solutions** folder.

Exercise 3.29

Sample solutions for this exercise are saved as Appointment Solution, Appointment Letters Solution and Questionnaire2 Solution in the Module 3 Solutions folder.

Spreadsheet Software

Exercise 4.1

Step 3   a) **AutoSum** or **Sum** b) **Copy** c) **Format Painter**

Step 4   **Standard** toolbar (*XP/2003*) or **Insert** tab (*2007/2010/2013*)

Exercise 4.2

Step 2   **3** worksheets by default

Step 3   Cell **A2** (unless the **Excel Options** have been changed)

Step 4   a) **Align (Text) Left** b) **Merge and Center** c) **Fill Color**

Step 5   <**End** →> or <**Ctrl** →>

Step 6   **65536** (*XP/2003*) or **1048576** (*2007/2010/2013*)

Step 7   <**Ctrl Home**>

Step 8   <**Alt Page Down**>

Step 9   **255** columns (*XP/2003*) or **16,384** (*2007/2010/2013*)

Exercise 4.3

Step 2   Cell **N31**

Step 3   Range of Booking block **Q3:AF9**

Step 4   **35%**

Step 6   Payments

Step 8   **9800**

Exercise 4.4

Step 4   Market Stall

Step 7   Temperatures

Step 9   Cell **N15**

Step 10   The key press is <**Ctrl Home**>

Exercise 4.5

Step 1   Because each cell should only contain one element of data. So there should be separate cells for each line of address and for data such as Town and Country.

Sample solutions for this exercise are saved as Viewing Solution, Viewing csv Solution and snackdata solution in the Module 4 Solutions folder.

Exercise 4.6

Step 1   False. When creating lists you should avoid blank rows and columns in the main body of the list. Insert blank rows only before a total row and ensure cells surrounding the list are blank.

A sample solution for this exercise is saved as **Adelaide Weather Solution.htm** in the **Module 4 Solutions** folder.

Exercise 4.7

Step 2   **49**

Step 3   **37**

Step 5   Column of numbers, 143

Step 6   **143**. **Yes** the answers are the same

Step 8   **#NAME**. The name **total** is invalid in the formula

Step 10   **#DIV/0**. Dividing by zero is invalid

Step 11   **#REF** The original referenced cell **E8** has been removed

A sample solution for this exercise is saved as **Courses Solution** in the **Module 4 Solutions** folder.

Exercise 4.8

Step 6   **2225** profit

Step 7   **John** made the most profit for the company, 545

Step 10   If cell references are used the formula will always be correct and updated if the data in the cell changes

A sample solution for this exercise is saved as **Computer Sales Solution** in **Module 4 Solutions**.

Exercise 4.9

Step 2   c) more than 1000 under - too pessimistic

Step 7   It's better to replace the default name with a meaningful name

A sample solution for this exercise is saved as **Forecast2 Solution** in the **Module 4 Solutions** folder.

Exercise 4.10

A sample solution for this exercise is saved as **Divisions2 Solution** in the **Module 4 Solutions** folder.

Exercise 4.11

Step 5   14.55

Step 9   1.40 short

A sample solution for this exercise is saved as **Petty Cash Feb Solution** in the **Module 4 Solutions** folder.

Exercise 4.12

Step 3   -25

Step 4   Ali

Step 7   Numbers are sorted first

Step 9   4 replacements were made

Step 11   2AC

Step 12   Case has no effect when being sorted

Exercise 4.14

Step 2   The worksheet is previewed over 6 pages

Exercise 4.15

Step 6   88900

Step 7   New York

Step 8   Saturday

A sample solution for this exercise is saved as **Theatre2 Solution** in the **Module 4 Solutions** folder.

Exercise 4.16

Step 9   The orientation is **Portrait** and it has **2** pages

A sample solution for this exercise is saved as **Market Stall Formatted Solution** in the **Module 4 Solutions** folder.

Exercise 4.17

Step 10   The Average is **1244.37**

A sample solution for this exercise is saved as **Stationery Sales Solution** in the **Module 4 Solutions** folder.

Exercise 4.18

Step 4   The average mark is 60

Step 5   The average now is 64

Step 16   14 passes

A sample solution for this exercise is saved as **Results2 Solution** in the **Module 4 Solutions** folder.

Exercise 4.19

Step 4   The row will not adjust automatically because the row was manually adjusted in step 3

A sample solution for this exercise is saved as **Chart Solution** in the **Module 4 Solutions** folder.

Exercise 4.20

Step 4   **Sydney** with an average temperature of **19.4**

Step 15   Toronto has a colder winter but a warmer summer compared to London

A sample solution for this exercise is saved as **Temperature Chart Solution** in the **Module 4 Solutions** folder.

Exercise 4.21

Step 6   3 dogs are Labradors

A sample solution for this exercise is saved as **Dogs Solution** in the **Module 4 Solutions** folder.

Exercise 4.22

Step 14   The percentage profit is **20.3%**

A sample solution for this exercise is saved as **Holiday Cottages Solution** in **Module 4 Solutions**.

Exercise 4.23

Step 13   The best selling wine is the **Riesling White** (stock code **W02**)

A sample solution for this exercise is saved as **Wine Warehouse Solution** in the **Module 4 Solutions** folder.

Exercise 4.24

Step 3   There are **26** entries

Step 6   The prize fund is **1800**

Step 9   The **First Place** prize money is **39%** of the total

A sample solution for this exercise is saved as **Tournament Results Solution** in the **Module 4 Solutions** folder.

Exercise 4.25

A sample solution for this exercise is saved as **World Cup2 Solution** in the **Module 4 Solutions** folder.

Exercise 4.26

Step 7   **60cm**. Tanks 5 and 6

Step 8   **6** tanks are too small

Step 10   Cost is **65**

Step 11   **Tank 10** is the biggest you can afford. **Angel** fish - not enough depth, **Clown Barb** not enough volume of water and probably the **Discus** fish as it needs a large tank.

Step 18   The tank is **47%** of the cost

A sample solution for this exercise is saved as **Tropical Fish Solution** in the **Module 4 Solutions** folder.

Database Software

Exercise 5.1

Step 1   A database is a structured collection of records or data stored in a computer system

Step 2   Data is an organised collection of information, the raw material; information is data that has been processed to be meaningful

Step 3   Examples include airline booking systems, government records, bank account records and hospital patient details

Step 4   A database is organised in tables which contain records and fields

Step 7   There are **2** tables, **Computers** and **Repairs**

Step 8   **AutoNumber** primary keys, **Single-field** primary keys, and **Multiple-field** primary keys

Step 10   a) – **Sort Ascending** (**Ascending** in *2007/2010/2013*)

            b) – **Filter by Selection** (**Selection** in *2007/2010/2013*)

Step 11   There is **1** macro

Step 12   **c**, both *Access* and the database will close

Exercise 5.2

Step 1   A database specialist designs and creates professional databases

Step 2   Normal database users perform data entry, data maintenance and information retrieval

Step 3   A database administrator provides access to specific data for appropriate users and is responsible for recovery of a database after a crash or major errors

Step 7   **40** records. This value is shown next to the navigation buttons

Step 8   **14** fields for each record

Step 9   12 Desert Road

Step 10   **c** and **d**, adding a new field and changing the column width

Exercise 5.3

Step 1   No. Each table should contain data related to a single subject

Step 2   It may affect data already in the table

Step 5   Data type changed to **Text** and field size changed to **6**

Step 6   The primary key must provide a unique reference to the record

Step 12   **CH004** is the first record because the table is indexed on the primary key field (course ID)

A sample solution for this exercise is saved as **Learning Solution** in the **Module 5 Solutions** folder (the **Courses** table is included for reference).

Exercise 5.4

Step 1   Each field should only contain one element of data

Step 4   The generated primary key is an **AutoNumber** field called **ID**

Step 11   Records are displayed in **Room No** order because they are indexed on this field

A sample solution for this exercise is saved as **Hotel Solution** in the **Module 5 Solutions** folder.

Exercise 5.5

Step 1   Tables are related to help prevent duplication of data

Step 7   There are 3 bookings for apartment **B8**

Step 9   **You cannot add or change a record because a related record is required in table 'Apartments'**, i.e. there is no B9 record in the apartments table. This is caused by the referential integrity setting

A sample solution for this exercise is saved as **Sunshine Solution** in the **Module 5 Solutions** folder.

Exercise 5.6

Step 1   A relationship is built by matching a unique field in one table with a field in another table

Step 5   Options **a**, **c** and **d** are true, only **b** is false

Step 7   **Jason Myers** has 14 claims but only for **2** different projects

Step 9   The relationship is one-to-one because **Staff No** is the primary key in each table and therefore must be unique in each table

A sample solution for this exercise is saved as **Consultants Solution** in the **Module 5 Solutions** folder.

Exercise 5.7

Step 4   Match setting is **Any Part of Field**. **2** records are found

Step 5   Key press is **<Ctrl '>** (control and apostrophe together)

A sample solution for this exercise is saved as **Beauty Solution** in the **Module 5 Solutions** folder.

Exercise 5.8

Step 5   John Weston lives at 5 Orchard Drive

Step 7   Vera Elliot, Mandy Williams, Paul Bright and Barry Robson all joined on 14/04/2001

A sample solution for this exercise is saved as **Club Solution** in the **Module 5 Solutions** folder.

Exercise 5.9

Step 3   **27.50**

Step 4   27/12/2010

Step 6   **130** records are for expenses other than mileage

Step 7   **11** records are for expenses greater than 1000

Step 8   Employee **112** has submitted a claim for entertaining against Global

Exercise 5.10

Step 3   There are **32** premises not in the Central Area

Step 5   **6 Shore Road** is the least expensive property in the Riverside Complex

Step 6   **17** properties are **Office Premises** and of them, **M017** has the largest area

Step 8   The previous filter is reapplied, the previous sort is not

Step 9   **8** unoccupied properties are priced at more than 100,000

Exercise 5.11

Step 11   **18** claims are for 582.40

A sample solution for this exercise is included in the **Expenses Solution** in the **Module 5 Solutions** folder (**Check** query has been left for reference).

Exercise 5.12

Step 2   Queries are used mainly to extract and analyse data from database tables

A sample solution for this exercise is included in the **Central Solution** in the **Module 5 Solutions** folder (**Floors** query has been left in for reference).

Exercise 5.13

Step 4   Forms are used mainly to display and maintain individual records

Step 7

XP/2003

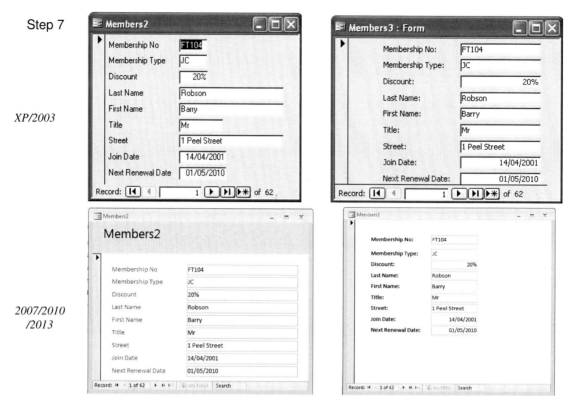

2007/2010
/2013

A sample solution for this exercise is included in **Club Solution** in the **Module 5 Solutions** folder.

Exercise 5.14

Step 7   There should be about five records on a page, depending on the size of the form

Step 9   Premises ID **P009** is first

Step 11   **M012** is now first

Step 12   1 Wessington Road

Step 13   Unit D, Main Building

Step 15   There are 5 filtered records

A sample solution for this exercise is included in **Central Solution** in the **Module 5 Solutions** folder.

Exercise 5.15

Step 5   In XP/2003 **Date** and **Page Number** are shown by default in the page footer. In *2007/2010/2013* only **Page Number** is shown.

A sample solution for this exercise is included in **Expenses Solution** in the **Module 5 Solutions** folder. A sample of the exported file **Staffing.txt** is also available.

Exercise 5.16

Step 3   Property **PO15** is the cheapest in **DockLand**

Step 4   Grand totals are for all records regardless of how they are grouped so should be the same

A sample solution for this exercise is included in **Central Solution** in the **Module 5 Solutions** folder (**Type** report has been left for reference).

Exercise 5.17

Step 1   Bookings are increasing year by year

Step 15   One to one link is created. Atomic number is a primary key (and therefore unique) in both tables.

Step 19

List						
Classification	*Atomic Number*	*Name*	*Symbol*	*Atomic Mass*	*Melting Point*	*Boiling Point*
Gas						
	10	Neon	Ne	20	-249	-246
	2	Helium	He	4	-272	-269
	1	Hydrogen	H	1	-259	-253
	7	Nitrogen	N	14	-210	-196

A sample solution for this exercise is saved as **Chemistry Solution** in the **Module 5 Solutions** folder.

Exercise 5.18

Step 1   b) Calculation of office accounts

A sample solution for this exercise is saved as **Hire Solution** in the **Module 5 Solutions** folder.

Exercise 5.19

Step 1   Separate into 3 linked tables to hold customer, products and order information

Step 2   Because each field should only contain one element of data, e.g. quantity or item

Step 4   ▶| . Yes, the same button applies in queries and form

A sample solution for this exercise is saved as **Wages Solution** in the **Module 5 Solutions** folder.

Exercise 5.20

Step 1   c) Database Administrator

Step 6   Because **Month** is a text field and is therefore sorted alphabetically

Step 12   **Thraddle** production exceeded **4000** in **March**

Step 15   **November** has the highest total (12,928) and the overall output for the year is 119,559

A sample solution for this exercise is saved as **Production Solution** in **Module 5 Solutions**.

Exercise 5.21

Step 2   Mount Kenya was first climbed in 1899

Step 4   They are all in Asia

Step 7   6 of the mountains listed are between 5000 and 7000 metres high

Step 10   6 records can be viewed

A sample solution for this exercise is saved as **Geography Solution** in **Module 5 Solutions**.

Presentation Software

Exercise 6.1

Step 3   The **<F1>** key

Step 4   **Slide Show**

Step 5   In the panel on the left of **Normal View** after clicking the **Outline** tab

Step 6   a) **Format Painter**, b) **Text Shadow** (or **Shadow**), c) **Bullets**, d) **Center**

Step 9   Any from this list:

- Use short concise statements
- Avoid clutter
- Use bullet points
- Use numbered lists
- Use sympathetic colour schemes
- Use relevant graphics

Exercise 6.2

Step 6   Re-colours the picture.

Exercise 6.3

Sample solutions for this exercise are saved as Computers2 Solution, Computers Show Solution, Kennel Template Solution and Computers3 Solution in the Module 6 Solutions folder.

Exercise 6.4

Step 1   Title Slide.

Step 6   Different slide titles will help to identify each slide uniquely, especially when using views such as outline view or slide show view.

Sample solutions for this exercise are saved as **Solar System Solution** and **Planets Solution** in the **Module 6 Solutions** folder.

Exercise 6.5

A sample solution for this exercise is saved as **Computer Formatted Solution** in the **Module 6 Solutions** folder.

Exercise 6.6

A sample solution for this exercise is saved as **Shower Formatted Solution** in the **Module 6 Solutions** folder.

Exercise 6.7

A sample solution for this exercise is saved as **Images Solution** in the **Module 6 Solutions** folder.

Exercise 6.8

Step 9

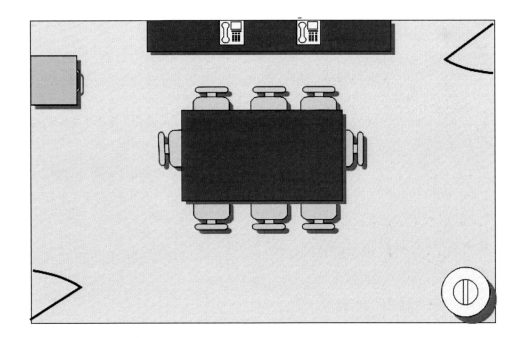

A sample solution for this exercise is saved as **Shower2 Solution** in the **Module 6 Solutions** folder.

Exercise 6.9

A sample solution for this exercise is saved as **Figures Solution** in the **Module 6 Solutions** folder.

Exercise 6.10

Sample solutions for this exercise are saved as **Computers4 Solution** and **Computers5 Solution** in the **Module 6 Solutions** folder.

Exercise 6.11

A sample solution for this exercise is saved as **Ocean Fish Solution** in the **Module 6 Solutions** folder.

Exercise 6.12

A sample solution for this exercise is saved as **Computer Parts Solution** in the **Module 6 Solutions** folder.

Exercise 6.13

Sample solutions for this exercise are saved as **Football Solution** and **Football Show Solution** in the **Module 6 Solutions** folder.

Exercise 6.14

Sample solutions for this exercise are saved as **Invention Template Solution** in the **Module 6 Solutions** folder.

Exercise 6.15

Sample solutions for this exercise are saved as **Flag Quiz Complete Solution** and **Flags Brief Solution** in the **Module 6 Solutions** folder.

Exercise 6.16

Sample solutions for this exercise are saved as **Sport Solution** and **sports clips solution** in the **Module 6 Solutions** folder.

Exercise 6.17

A sample solution for this exercise is saved as **Kennels Solution** in the **Module 6 Solutions** folder.